# INTRODUCTION TO DIGITAL ELECTRONICS

# INTRODUCTION TO DIGITAL ELECTRONICS

*STANLEY M. HAJEK*

Delmar Publishers Inc.®

*Cover photo courtesy of Gould Electronics, Semiconductor Division*

*Delmar staff*
Administrative editor: Mark Huth
Associate editor: Jonathan Plant
Production editor: Ruth Saur
Art Director: Ronald Blackman
Design Coordinator: John Orozco

For information, address Delmar Publishers Inc.
2 Computer Drive West, Box 15-015
Albany, New York 12212-9985

Printed in the United States of America
Published simultaneously in Canada
by Nelson Canada,
A division of International Thomson Limited

10 9 8 7 6 5 4 3 2 1

**Library of Congress Cataloging in Publication Data**

Hajek, Stanley.
 Introduction to digital electronics.

 Includes index.
 1. Digital electronics. I. Title.
TK7868.D5H295    1986    621.3815    85-20554
ISBN 0-8273-2373-5
ISBN 0-8273-2374-3 (instructor's guide)
ISBN 0-8273-2615-7 (lab. manual)

# CONTENTS

# PREFACE

INTRODUCTION TO DIGITAL ELECTRONICS is intended to give students an understanding of the electronics that are used in computers and computer peripheral equipment. This text is written so that it could be used in computer literacy classes, computer science classes, industrial arts and technology education classes. Knowledge of electronics is not prerequisite to understanding the digital electronics in this text. The information necessary to understand the electronic circuits used is provided as needed.

The chapters in INTRODUCTION TO DIGITAL ELECTRONICS are easy to comprehend because of the concise but comprehensive coverage of each subject and the numerous illustrations that are closely correlated with the text material. To further enhance the readability of the text, unfamiliar words are italicized and defined in the glossary.

Each of the 15 chapters starts with a listing of the objectives to be learned in the chapter and an overview of the subject matter. Each chapter ends with a summary of what should have been learned. Thus, the student is informed as to what is to be learned before reading the chapter and can check to see what has been learned when the chapter is finished. Highlighted special features are interspersed throughout the book. These offer general information on new technology, history, and other areas of interest.

Review questions are provided at the end of each chapter to aid the student and the instructor in determining if the material has been comprehended. Activities are suggested at the end of chapters to stimulate interest and provide hands-on experiences which promote retention of the chapter material. With the information learned in Chapter 15 and specification sheets in the appendix, many worthwhile electronic devices can be built that will add excitement to learning digital electronics.

A laboratory manual with interesting, enlightening, and fun experiments is coordinated with this text to provide reinforcement of the subject matter and to aid retention of the information. The hands-on approach is definitely provided by the combination of text and lab manual.

## ACKNOWLEDGMENTS

I wish to express my appreciation to my wife Ellen, without whose assistance this project would not have been attempted, and to my son Mike for his patience while I was working on this text. I would also like to thank the many reviewers of this text for their valuable input and my colleagues and school administrators for their support. Appreciation is also expressed to the companies that provided photographs used in the text.

S.H.

## ABOUT THE AUTHOR

Stanley Hajek received his undergraduate degree from Peru State College in Nebraska, and a Master's Degree in Industrial Arts from the University of Northern Colorado. He has more than twenty years' teaching experience at the high school and junior high school levels. Currently, Mr. Hajek teaches at Golden Senior High School in Golden, Colorado.

# 1

# USING ELECTRICITY SAFELY

## OBJECTIVES

After studying this chapter, you will be able to:
- Recognize dangers involved in using electricity.
- Follow safe practices when using electricity.

## OVERVIEW

Anyone who works with electricity or electrical devices should be aware of the danger of electrical shock. This chapter describes the effect of electrical shock upon the human body and suggests safe practices to follow when working with electricity.

## ELECTRICAL SHOCK

*Electricity* may be defined as the movement of electrons through a material. It is one of humanity's most valuable discoveries. To use electricity safely, it must be handled properly. A person who is careless around electrical devices may suffer *electrical shock*, which can be harmful or even fatal.

*Electrons* are the smallest parts of an atom; they revolve around the atom's nucleus. When electrons move through the human body, the body suffers electrical shock. The increased electron flow overrides the minute electrical impulses that usually control body muscles and cause injury to nerves and tissues. Electrical shock can also cause muscles to contract and lock into position. A person who receives an electrical shock from a device he or she has taken hold of may not be able to let go because the electric current has caused the hands to lock onto it.

Body tissues have a certain amount of resistance or opposition to the movement of electrons. As electrons are forced through this resistance, heat is created that can cause severe burns. To some extent the skin can oppose the movement of electrons through it. Skin resistance is much higher than the resistance of other body tissues. However, wet skin is 10 to over 100 times less resistant to electrons than dry skin. It is important to keep skin resistance high by working only in dry conditions.

### Effects on the Heart

One of the most serious forms of electrical shock occurs when the electricity passes through the heart. Just as other muscles react when exposed to electrical shock, the heart may contract. If it stays contracted, it cannot pump blood to the parts of the body where it is needed.

In some cases electricity passing through the heart disrupts the minute electrical impulses that keep it beating rhythmically. The heart begins to beat very irregularly and does not perform the pumping action it is supposed to do. This irregular heartbeat is called *fibrillation*.

### Voltage

*Voltage* is the pressure that pushes electricity. How much body tissues are damaged by electrical shock depends upon how much voltage the body is subjected to and for what length of time. The longer the body is subjected to electrical current, the more damage the body suffers, Figure 1-1.

Electricity from a wall outlet (called *line voltage*) is usually 120 volts. This voltage can be dangerous. A lower voltage, such as the 5 to 12 volts

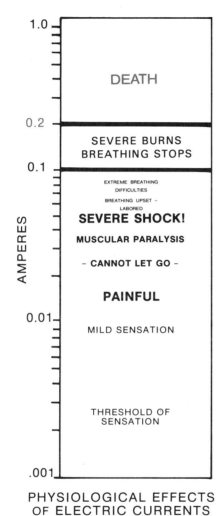

PHYSIOLOGICAL EFFECTS
OF ELECTRIC CURRENTS

**Figure 1-1.** How electrical shock affects
the human body (courtesy of Graymark
International Inc.)

from a battery presents little danger of serious shock. However, even though digital electronic circuits require only 5 volts to operate properly, the low voltage is often obtained by stepping down the voltage from a 120-volt source. This type of circuit can be dangerous if not used properly. Fortunately, many of the electronic devices today are battery operated.

## SAFETY PRACTICES

Being aware of how dangerous electricity can be is only the first step in protecting yourself from danger. You must also follow safe procedures anywhere that electricity is present. Just as with other potentially dangerous situations, it is important dealing with electricity to think before acting and to be careful at all times.

Other safety practices to keep in mind are the following:

1. Work with electrical devices only in dry conditions. Remember that resistance goes down in most objects when they are wet.
2. Be sure that all electrical tools and equipment are properly *grounded* (equipped with a wire that provides a path for electrons to flow to earth). Grounding helps prevent accidental electrical shock. Manufacturers provide for grounding by using an electrical plug that has a third wire. The prong that is connected to the grounding wire should never be removed.
3. Always unplug electrical devices before attempting to repair them. Because television sets retain a high voltage even after they have been unplugged, only a qualified technician should work on them.
4. Allow hot electrical devices to cool before handling them. Some electrical devices get extremely hot, especially large resistors that are designed to carry away heat. Also, vacuum tubes must be hot to operate properly. Since it is easy to get burned by hot equipment, be sure to allow time for the electrical devices to reach a comfortable temperature before doing any work on them.
5. Avoid contact with hot solder. Many electrical connections are made with solder. The soldering pencil or soldering gun gets very hot at the tip in order to melt the solder. Avoid contact with the heated parts of the soldering pencil or gun when you are not using it by setting the pencil in a holder or by placing the soldering gun well in front of you on the counter. Figure 1–2 shows the proper way to store a soldering pencil. A new solder joint is also very hot. Allow it to cool before handling it. Hot solder can cause severe injury if it gets into the eyes. To prevent injury, always wear safety glasses when soldering or desoldering.
6. Protect eyes, face, hands, and clothing when working with chemicals such as battery acid. Also protect eyes when grinding, drilling, or doing work where chips may fly. Use the proper tool for each job, and remove any sharp edges by filing them smooth.
7. Know the location of first aid materials, and be sure to get attention for any injuries, no matter how minor, Figure 1–3.

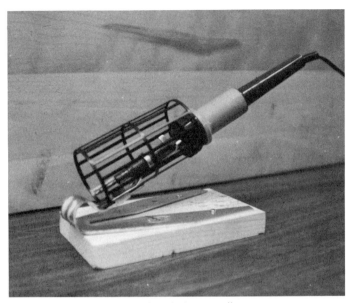

**Figure 1-2.** Safe storage of soldering pencils

In summary, the movement of electrons through the body can cause
damage to nerves and tissues. The higher the voltage, the greater the
number of electrons that can move through the body. The higher the
resistance, the fewer the number of electrons that can move through the
body. Since it is the movement of electrons that does the damage, it is
important to avoid contact with any voltage, especially a high voltage, and
to keep skin resistance high by working only in dry conditions. You should
understand the physiological effects of electrical shock upon the human
body and know and practice the safety rules that will help you avoid it.

You should now be aware that it is important to work carefully around
electricity. Among safe practices you will be sure to follow are these:

- avoid using electricity in damp places
- unplug electrical devices before attempting to repair them
- make certain that electrical devices are properly grounded before you use
  them

In addition, you should know and practice the safety rules that will help you
to avoid cuts, burns, and eye injuries.

---

## FIRST AID KIT

---

Emergency phone numbers
Reminder card for artificial respiration and CPR, First Aid Priorities
Pencil, pen, paper
Bandaids—#100 1″ size, large size #10–15
*Tourniquet—triangular bandage, dowel (1/2″ × 6″)
Compresses—4 × 4 #25–50
Roller bandages (2–3″) #5
Tape
*Constricting band
*Burn ointment (1st degree burns only)
Large sterile cloth (for large burn areas)
Soap or cleansing wipes
Blanket
*Salt, baking soda, water
*Ice, cold spray, instant cold, etc.
Triangular bandages
Scissors, tweezers, safety pins
Alcohol, matches

---

*Use of these items can be more harmful than good if improperly used. For instruction contact your local Red Cross chapter.

**Figure 1–3.** Materials needed for first aid (courtesy of Jefferson Region Red Cross Volunteers)

## REVIEW QUESTIONS

1. Explain the two ways the heart might react when electrons flow through it.
2. Explain why it is important to work with electrical devices only in dry conditions.
3. You should always wear _____ to protect yourself when soldering.
4. Name two components that become hot after they have been in use for a period of time.
5. What danger may still be present in a television set even though it is turned off and unplugged?
6. What precautions should be taken when using a chemical such as sulfuric acid?

## SUGGESTED ACTIVITIES

1. Locate first aid kits in your home and in your electronics work area and examine what they contain so that you are familiar with them.
2. Consult a school nurse or other authority for information about any first aid material with which you may not be familiar.

# 2

# DEVELOPMENTS IN ELECTRONICS

## OBJECTIVES

After studying this chapter, you will be able to:
- List the significant developments in the field of electronics.
- Explain the difference between analog electronics and digital electronics.
- Describe the process for making integrated circuits.
- List numerous electronic devices and describe how their use has affected our society.
- List job groups in the electronics field and be aware of training needed for certain careers.

## OVERVIEW

In this chapter you will learn that the field of electronics evolved slowly for many years. It was considered a fairly small industry in comparison to giants such as steel making and automobile manufacturing. In the late sixties and early seventies the development of the integrated circuit caused an electronics revolution that has affected our society much as the Industrial Revolution did in the early 1900s.

*From the early process of putting one transistor on a piece of silicon by hand to the present process of placing a million or more components on a silicon chip through mass production techniques, the electronics industry has grown so rapidly that it is predicted to be the second largest industry in the United States by the year 2000. Only the energy industry will be larger.*

In the late 1800s, Thomas Edison was trying to develop the light bulb. The problem he had with the experimental light bulb was that the *filament* (the part that gives off light when heated) kept breaking under its own weight when it was hot. In order to keep the filament from breaking, Edison tried using a metal rod to support it. He found that electrons flowed from the heated filament to the support rod even though there was not an electrical conductor between them. This accidental discovery of what is called *thermionic emission* (giving off of electrons from a heated metal) led to the development of the vacuum tube.

At first, the vacuum tube was used only to change AC (alternating current) to DC (direct current). In 1912, Dr. Lee DeForest developed a *triode* (three-element) vacuum tube that was able to amplify an electronic signal. The triode was widely used in radios.

In 1949 engineers at Bell Laboratories invented the *transistor*. This solid-state device had many advantages over the vacuum tube because it was smaller, less fragile (no glass), and more durable (no heater to burn out). It operated on a lower voltage and did not require a heater voltage. Eventually, because of mass production techniques, the transistor became less expensive than the vacuum tube. Figure 2–1 shows the size of a transistor as compared to a vacuum tube.

During World War II, the army developed an electronic computer, the ENIAC, which was used to compute artillery and bomb trajectories. This computer was huge, especially when compared to today's microcomputers that have so much more capability. The ENIAC used 1800 vacuum tubes and filled a space 100 feet long and 10 feet high. It generated so much heat that the temperature in the room would reach 120 degrees.

When the transistor was developed, industry saw a solution to reducing the size and the operating temperature of computers. The first transistors were wired together individually by hand. This was a slow, expensive process since thousands of transistors were needed to make a computer, Figure 2–2.

One way to cut the cost of individual transistors was to make several on one piece of *silicon* and then cut them apart for use. In 1959 two

**BRIEF HISTORY OF ELECTRONICS**

**INTEGRATED CIRCUITS**

**Figure 2–1.** Size comparison of a transistor to a vacuum tube

engineers working independently of each other decided that if several transistors could be put on a silicon or *germanium* chip (germanium is another material used to make transistors), they could be interconnected on the chip to make a circuit. The engineers went a step further and found that almost all of the parts of an electronic circuit, *diodes, resistors*, and, to a limited extent, even *capacitors*, could be built into a silicon chip.

This electronic circuit on a chip was first announced by Jack Kilby of Texas Instruments, and he called it an *integrated circuit* (IC). Six months later Robert Noyce of Fairchild Semiconductors created a similar integrated circuit. Kilby's integrated circuit was made of germanium and Noyce's of silicon. It turned out that Noyce's integrated circuit was more efficient and more practical to produce, and it became the standard of the industry.

The integrated circuit, which the press called the *microchip*, is based upon the transistor. However, it made possible many electronics devices

**Figure 2-2.** The IBM 7030 computer, put on the market in 1960, contained nearly 150,000 transistors (courtesy of IBM Corporation).

that would not have been possible or even practical using individual transistors. The miniaturization that took place because of the integrated circuit made it possible to put all of the functions of the ENIAC on a panel the size of a playing card. It also made possible space travel, robots, and watches with numerical readout instead of hands.

The integrated circuit has undergone almost continuous change since it was first developed. The goal of integrated circuit designers has been to put more and more components on a single chip. Doing this increases reliability because most connections are a part of the chip. Speed of operations is increased because the electronic signal does not have to travel as far. Less power is required to operate the circuit as the components get smaller. Also, the cost of a particular complex circuit goes down because it can all be included in one package rather than in two or three. Labor and handling costs are also lower. The process of squeezing more and more components onto a single chip will probably continue for some time.

## Processing a Chip

It is hard to imagine that something as complex as an integrated circuit could be made from a material as simple and common as sand. However it is true that silicon, of which most ICs are made, is found in its natural form as sand and is the earth's second most abundant element.

Sand is processed to produce molten silicon. A seed crystal of either N-type or P-type material is dipped into the melt and is withdrawn under computer control to create a single crystal with all of the silicon atoms arranged in a uniform diamond lattice structure.

For every ten billion atoms, 9,999,999,999 must be silicon. Only one nonsilicon atom can be permitted. Imagine only one white golf ball in a string of yellow golf balls from here to the moon; that's roughly equivalent to one atom of impurity in 10 billion atoms of silicon.

The crystals are cut into thin wafers (about the thickness of a razor blade) and polished smooth to within a few microns (millionths of an inch). Wafers are loaded into furnaces and exposed to oxygen, forming a glossy layer of silicon dioxide on the outside. The purity, thickness, and uniformity of the oxide layer must be precise since the minute electronic circuits will be formed through holes in this layer. A photosensitive

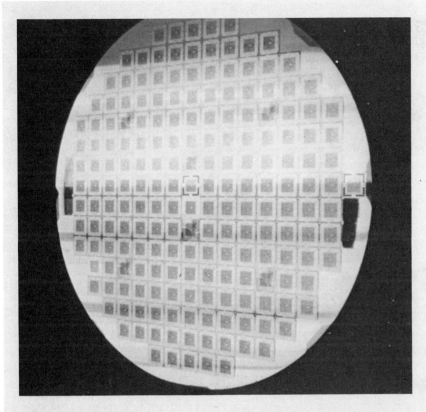

VLSI logic wafer. Each chip contains over 140,000 circuits (courtesy of IBM Corporation).

emulsion is placed onto each wafer, and under centrifugal force, the photoresist spreads evenly across the entire surface.

A high-precision glass mask is placed over the photoresist-coated, oxide-covered silicon. The pattern for the glass masks is designed using a Computer Aided Design system. The glass mask containing the tiny patterns is precisely registered over its target area in specially designed aligners. These aligners use closed circuit television cameras peering through high-power microscopes. Ultraviolet light is then transmitted through the clear mask areas, hardening the light-sensitive photoresist. The part of the photoresist that was protected by the mask remains unexposed. The unexposed photoresist can then be chemically removed.

Since cleanliness is extremely vital to the crucial photo alignment process, the technician working with these materials wears special lint-free garments to minimize contamination of the work areas. The air in the

The glass mask is being inspected
(courtesy of IBM Corporation)

rooms where ICs are produced is filtered so that it is about 1000 times cleaner than a typical hospital operating room.

Through closed-circuit television, the operator can observe the mask under magnification and make alignments to within a few millionths of an inch. Misalignment can cause patterns to be placed too close to others and can cause the transistors to fail. Many of the steps in the process are carried out under yellow light because the photoresist is insensitive to it.

Acid that will etch through the oxide but not affect the remaining photoresist is used to open tiny windows in the wafer oxide layer. These windows correspond to the miniature rectangular shapes on the glass mask. Once the holes are etched in the oxide, the rest of the photoresist is stripped away.

Impurity atoms, such as phosphorus and boron, are diffused at high temperatures into the silicon wafer through the holes in the oxide. The

Designer at graphic terminal entering new chip design with a light pen. Chip design superimposed in the foreground (courtesy of IBM Corporation).

depth and concentration of these atoms governs the precise electrical properties of the transistors and other devices being developed in the silicon. This process is used to create electronic components like transistors, diodes and resistors. Components like transistors measure only a couple of thousandths of an inch square and are only a few millionths of an inch thick.

This cycle of processing is repeated many times, each time starting with a new layer of oxide. Different parts of the microminiature transistors and other devices are built in each subsequent pass through the steps. Accurate photo alignment is critical to this process.

Finally, the wafer has all the required electronic components built down into the surface of each of its chips. Throughout the whole process

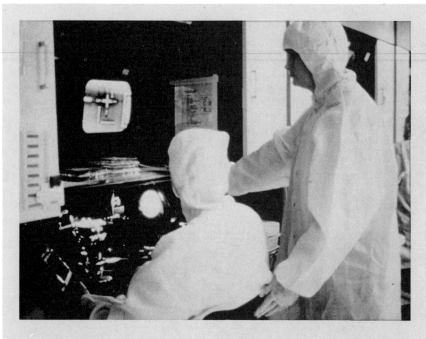

Viewing closed-circuit TV monitor, operators carefully align mask with wafer (courtesy of IBM Corporation).

of developing these IC wafers, sophisticated computers are monitoring all of the processes, and elaborate tests of each wafer are made to ensure that the finished product meets all quality control standards.

After all components have been diffused into the silicon, complex wiring patterns are added. Wafers are loaded on dome-shaped carriers and placed in vacuum chambers where a coating of copperdoped aluminum is applied by an evaporation process completely controlled by computer. This process is called evaporation because the copper/aluminum mixture is heated until it evaporates and is deposited on all surfaces.

Next, the unwanted copper/aluminum is selectively removed in another photo and etching process, leaving the desired interconnection wiring on the surface of each chip.

To electrically insulate and to seal the chip a quartz (gloss) layer is applied over the chip by a process called sputtering. In the sputtering process, a large quartz disk is bombarded with argon ions which causes silicon dioxide molecules to be dislodged and deposited throughout the vacuum chamber.

At this point, the tightly integrated circuits on each chip are completely "wired" up and they have been protected by the layer of sputtered quartz. Now the chips must be prepared for physical and electrical connection to the module substrate (material the chip is mounted on). Small holes are opened in the quartz layer and deposits of metal consisting of chrome, copper, gold and tin-lead are placed in each of the holes.

When the wafers are cut into individual chips, each chip is placed face down on the ceramic material it is to be mounted on and heated. Heat causes the lead solder that was deposited in the holes to melt and attach the chip to the circuit paths on the ceramic base material. These circuit paths connect the chip to the IC pins.

The process of cutting the wafers into individual chips is called dicing. The wafer is placed on a carrier paper similar to clear sticky tape. A computer-controlled diamond wheel cuts through the silicon but not through the carrier paper beneath. Although completely separated from each other, the chips remain stuck to the carrier.

A special tool picks the chips that have to this point in the processing tested good and removes them from the tape by a robotic arm which

Computer-monitored etch station removes unexposed coating on wafer surface leaving the desired circuit patterns (courtesy of IBM Corporation).

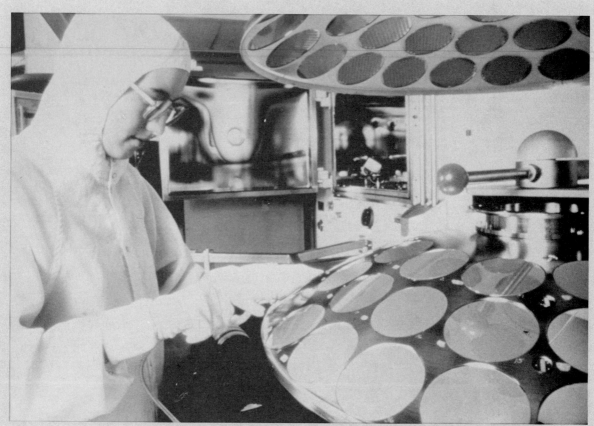

Evaporation metallurgy used to complete IBM integrated circuits (courtesy of IBM Corporation).

places them into tracks leading to spiral containers. In a subsequent step, the chips will "march" out of the spiral or helix and into the chip placement machine to be automatically positioned on a ceramic substrate.

The substrates have printed metal paths on or within the ceramic, which connects to the pins. As described earlier, the chips are fastened to the ceramic substrate. Next, the substrates containing the chips are coated with a protective sealant and an aluminum cap is placed over them. A numeric code identifying the chips is stamped on the cap. The bottom of the substrate is also sealed to give further protection.

After 100 percent testing, chips are placed in helix chip carrier for automated chip placement (courtesy of IBM Corporation).

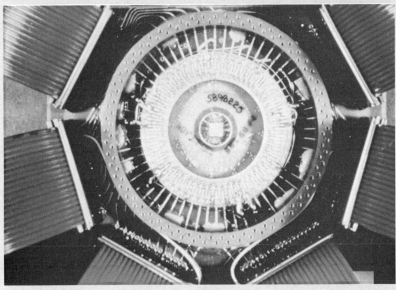

Every chip is automatically tested under computer control before being placed on a ceramic substrate (courtesy of IBM Corporation).

## Stages of Development

The stages of development of integrated circuits can be roughly classified into the following categories:

- small scale integration (SSI)—contains up to approximately 10 components per chip
- medium scale integration (MSI)—contains from 10 to approximately 100 components per chip
- large scale integration (LSI)—contains from 100 to approximately 1000 components per chip
- very large scale integration (VLSI)—contains over 1000 components per chip

Integrated circuits that contain more than a million components in what are called "superchips" are now available.

## HOW TRANSISTORS WORK

The process of making integrated circuits developed from the process of making transistors. Transistors basically do two things—amplify an electronic signal and act as a switch. A transistor amplifies because a small current between the emitter and base can control a large current between the collector and emitter, Figure 2–3. If there is no current flow in the base-emitter circuit, no current will flow in the collector-emitter circuit.

In the transistor circuit shown in Figure 2–4, the emitter of the transistor is a part of both the input and the output of the circuit. This means it is common to both the input and the output. In this circuit the small alternating current signal at the input causes the current between the base and the emitter to vary in proportion to it. The base-emitter current, in

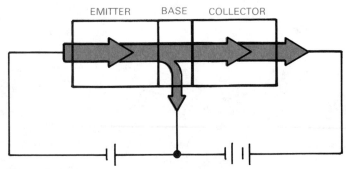

**Figure 2-3.** Current flow in a transistor

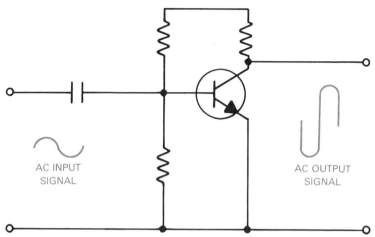

**Figure 2–4.** *Typical transistor circuit showing input and output signals*

turn, controls the emitter-collector current, which is much larger in value. In this particular circuit the output signal is inverted from the input signal, but there is both current gain and voltage gain. Because power gain is equal to current gain times voltage gain, there is a large increase in power.

## HOW TRANSISTORS ARE MADE

Most transistors are made of silicon, but other materials such as germanium are also used. Silicon is called a *semiconductor* material because it is neither a good conductor, nor is it a good nonconductor (insulator). By combining other materials with silicon, it is possible to change the atomic structure so that the combined material has more or fewer electrons in the outer ring of the atom than pure silicon, Figure 2–5.

Because electrons are negative charges, when silicon has been combined with a material such as phosphorus that has more electrons in its outer ring, the combined material appears negative and is called *N-type*. On the other hand, when silicon is combined with a material such as boron that has fewer electrons in its outer ring, the material appears positive when compared to pure silicon, and the material is called *P-type*.

A transistor is made up of three areas. Either the transistor has two outer areas of N-type material with P-type material sandwiched between them, or two outer areas of P-type material with N-type material sandwiched between them. Figure 2–6 shows the two types of transistors. It is obvious from the illustration why each transistor has its particular name. The three different parts of a transistor are labeled as shown in Figure 2–7.

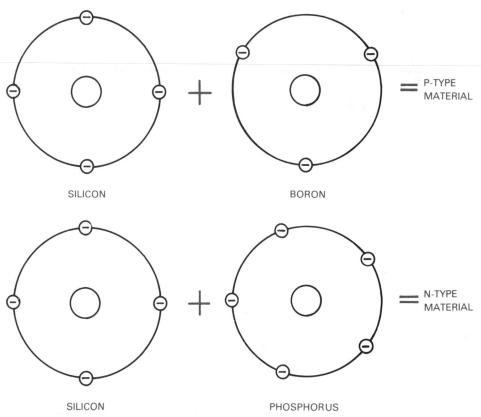

**Figure 2-5.** Atomic structures of silicon and elements it may be combined with to produce P-type or N-type materials.

## TRANSISTORS IN INTEGRATED CIRCUITS

Most integrated circuits contain transistors and are made by first forming an oxide layer on a silicon chip. Next, a layer of light-sensitive photoresist material is deposited on the oxide. An ultraviolet light is then directed through a patterned mask, allowing the photoresist to be exposed in selected areas. Figure 2–8 shows the ultraviolet light exposing the photoresist. When the photoresist is developed in etching solution, the parts that have been exposed to light are washed away. The parts of the oxide layer that are protected from light remain, as shown in Figure 2–9. The opening through the oxide is sometimes referred to as a window. The area of silicon directly below the opening in the oxide is specially treated to make it P-type material. The oxide layer prevents all but the exposed silicon from being treated.

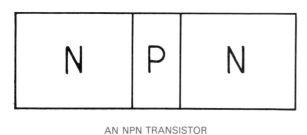

AN NPN TRANSISTOR

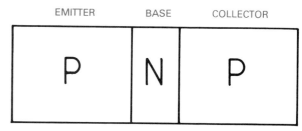

EMITTER          BASE          COLLECTOR

**Figure 2-7.** Diagram showing parts of a transistor

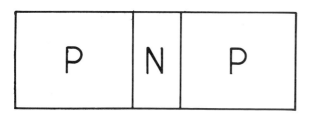

A PNP TRANSISTOR

**Figure 2-6.** Two types of transistors showing material of one composition sandwiched into material of another composition.

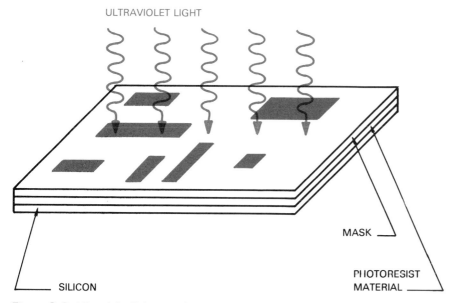

**Figure 2-8.** Ultraviolet light exposing photoresist material through holes in the mask

23

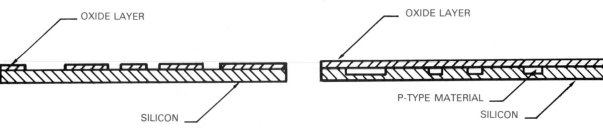

**Figure 2-9.** Parts of the oxide layer protected from light remain on the surface of the silicon.

**Figure 2-10.** New oxide layer formed over the P-type material and silicon

An oxide layer is again formed over the opening, making the silicon chip appear as shown in Figure 2–10. The entire process is repeated. However, this time a smaller opening in the mask above the P-type material allows a section of the P-type to be treated to make it N-type, as shown in Figure 2–11.

Finally, the process is repeated once more to form an area of P-type silicon within the small area of N-type silicon, Figure 2–12. In this final process the oxide layer is etched away again—this time to allow metal to be deposited in order for electrical contacts to be made to the emitter, base, and collector, Figure 2–13. The metal that is deposited to make electrical contacts can be used to interconnect transistors on the integrated circuit, or wires may be fastened to this metal to make connections to the external pins of the integrated circuit (IC).

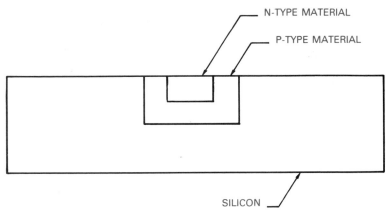

**Figure 2-11.** Layers of P- and N-type material being built into an IC

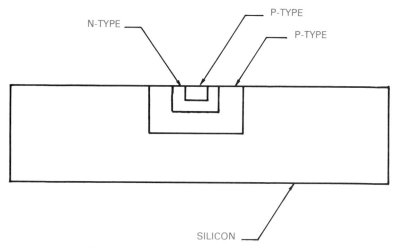

**Figure 2-12.** PNP transistor formed in an IC

*Diodes* are electronic devices similar to transistors, but they have only two rather than three parts. They are often used to change alternating current to direct current.

Diodes in ICs can be made in at least two ways. One way is to form an area of P-type and an area of N-type material, as shown in Figure 2-14. Another method is to use two elements of a transistor as a diode. Since all of the transistors on an IC are made at one time, an extra transistor is made for each diode needed in the circuit, and only two of the elements of each are

**DIODES IN INTEGRATED CIRCUITS**

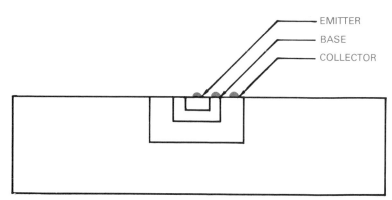

**Figure 2-13.** Metal deposits made for contacts to the emitter, base, and collector

N-TYPE MATERIAL

P-TYPE MATERIAL

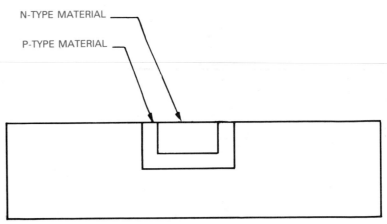

**Figure 2-14.** Diode in an IC made of P- and N-type materials

used. For example, the emitter-base or base-collector could be used for a diode, as shown in Figure 2–15.

**RESISTORS IN INTEGRATED CIRCUITS**

*Resistors* are devices used to control current flow. Resistors are also included in ICs. However, they take more space in an IC than do diodes or transistors because their length and cross-sectional areas are what determine their resistance values. Figure 2–16 shows two integrated circuit resistors—one of low resistance value and the other of high resistance value.

BASE

COLLECTOR

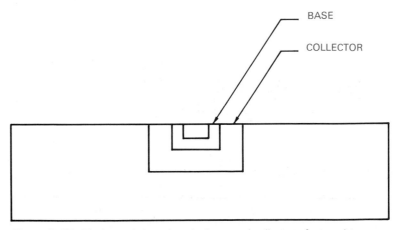

**Figure 2-15.** Diode made by using the base and collector of a transistor

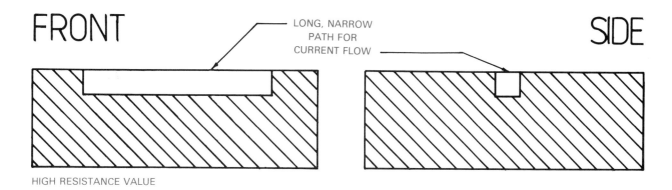

HIGH RESISTANCE VALUE

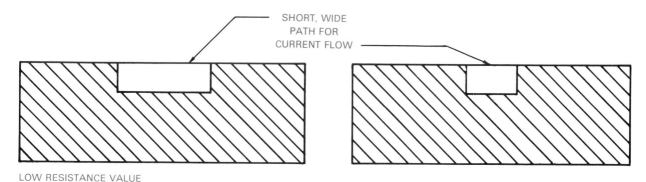

LOW RESISTANCE VALUE

**Figure 2-16.** Resistors in an integrated circuit

*Capacitors* are electronic components used to store electricity. They consist of conducting plates separated by an insulator. Only capacitors of small values can be formed in ICs because the value of a capacitor is dependent upon the size of its plates. In the IC, the P and N materials serve as the plates of the capacitor. If the junction between P-type and N-type material is connected so that current does not flow through it (reverse biased), it will serve as the insulator between the two plates. *Reverse bias* is when the polarity of the voltage is connected so that it is very difficult for current to flow between the P-type and the N-type material. Another

**CAPACITORS IN INTEGRATED CIRCUITS**

method of forming a capacitor in an integrated circuit is to place an oxide layer between sections of the deposited layer of metal, as shown in Figure 2-17.

ICs must be made with great precision in order to fit a million or more components on a chip of silicon less than 1/4-inch square. Because the circuits have become very complex, engineers use computer-assisted drafting (CAD) to design them. In order to make the original large drawings of the IC layouts the necessary small size to expose the tiny areas of photoresist material properly, reducing lenses are used. (Reducing lenses work just the opposite to magnifying lenses.)

## CAREERS

The growth in the number of devices using digital electronics has created diverse career opportunities. These opportunities can be divided into two major categories—repair and production.

People who do repairing provide regular maintenance, troubleshoot, replace or repair components and circuit boards, and, in some cases, make modifications to existing devices. People who work in production create or invent new devices, build prototypes of devices, or are involved in manufacturing and installation of such devices.

### Repair People

Although all digital electronics repair people must have a good knowledge of digital electronics, there are so many different devices that technicians specialize in particular areas. Some become computer service

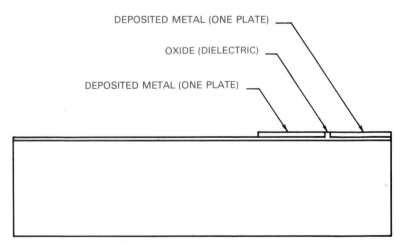

**Figure 2-17.** One method of forming a small value capacitor on an IC

technicians; biomedical equipment technicians; business machine service technicians; telephone and other communications equipment technicians; television, video, and audio technicians; vending machine technicians; robot technicians, etc. Vocational schools, military schools, and training programs offered by major companies provide good ways for a person to acquire the skills and knowledge necessary to become a repair technician.

## Production People

Production people can be classified into four major categories—electronics assemblers, electronics technicians, engineering technicians, and electrical engineers.

**Electronics Assemblers.**  Electronics assemblers build electronics devices from robots to video recorders and television to radar equipment. Some assemblers build the actual components, like ICs and transistors that go into electronic devices. Others assemble the components on boards, build control panels, and assemble the chassis into enclosures. Most assemblers do not need formal training; however, a high school diploma is generally required, and an interest and basic knowledge of electronics is helpful.

**Electronics Technicians.**  Electronics technicians help develop, test, modify, and install electronic devices of all kinds. They set up test equipment to test subassemblies and assembled electronic devices during the manufacturing process. They also have the responsibility of installing electronic devices and making final checks on them before they are available to the customer. Electronics technicians require classroom instruction and hands-on training. A college degree is not usually necessary although it can be helpful. One or two years of technical school training is usually adequate.

**Engineering Technicians.**  Engineering technicians assist engineers in all phases of engineering work from research and design to production, modification, and inspection of electronic devices. They devise and oversee tests of devices in production and final installation. They help develop and test prototype devices and analyze data from these tests, which provide a basis to develop new designs or modify old ones. Individuals working as engineering technicians should have at least two years of post-high-school training in electronics.

**Electrical Engineers.**  Electrical engineers do research and develop processes to design, manufacture, and test electrical devices. They gather and analyze data and then apply this information in the design of electronic products which may include laser communication devices, computer robots, microwave devices, avionics equipment (*avionics* is the name given to electronic devices on airplanes and other space vehicles), etc. Engineers are responsible for testing components and equipment to ensure that they operate according to specifications. To be an engineer requires graduation from a four-year school of engineering. Many engineers go on to earn master's degrees in engineering. Engineers can earn more money than engineering technicians to compensate them for the additional education required and the added responsibilities.

### Job Outlook

The job outlook in the field of electronics should grow at least as fast as average because of the increasing demand for electronic devices. Because so many digital electronic devices are being developed, the number of jobs for technicians is soaring and the pay is very good. Through the 1990s, and probably beyond that, engineers will be in great demand, especially those who know both computer hardware and software.

## SUMMARY

From reading this chapter, you should know that transistors have many advantages over vacuum tubes. For instance, they are smaller, less expensive, less fragile, do not require a heater voltage, and operate on a lower voltage.

Integrated circuits developed from the idea that more than one transistor could be built into a silicon chip. Once the process of putting several transistors on one chip and interconnecting them was developed, ICs rapidly replaced transistors in computer circuits. The development of this process led the way for miniaturization. Large patterns were made of IC layouts and then reduced photographically. Many of the electronic devices we take for granted would not have developed without the miniaturization that has taken place since the development of the IC. Digital watches, calculators, and portable computers all use integrated circuits and are dependent upon digital electronics to operate. The development of miniaturization has opened large, new career fields for the design, development, and repair of electronic devices.

## REVIEW QUESTIONS

1. What was Thomas Edison trying to develop when he accidentally discovered the theory of operation of a vacuum tube?
2. Dr. Lee DeForest developed a type of vacuum tube called the _____.
3. In 1949 the transistor was developed at the _____ laboratories.
4. Explain how the first simple integrated circuits differed from an ordinary transistor.
5. Approximately how many transistors does the MSI integrated circuit contain?
6. List the three parts of a transistor.
7. Explain how a P-N junction diode could be made in an integrated circuit.
8. In an integrated circuit, which resistor would have the greater resistance—a long, narrow one or a short, wide one?
9. Jobs in the production area of electronics can be broken down into four different groups. List these four groups.
10. What type of training is usually necessary to become a repair technician.

## SUGGESTED ACTIVITIES

1. Find a newspaper or magazine article about a new development in electronics, and bring it to school to share with your class.
2. Secure an old, burned-out IC and carefully remove the top half so that you can see the silicon chip. Use a microscope to observe the circuitry on the silicon chip.

# 3

# NUMBER SYSTEMS USED BY COMPUTERS

## OBJECTIVES

After studying this chapter, you will be able to:
- Describe various number systems used for counting.
- Convert a numerical value from one number system to another.

## OVERVIEW

Computers and many other electronic devices use number systems other than the familiar base 10 system. This chapter describes those systems and discusses why they are used in digital electronics.

The *binary* (base 2) system is well suited to use in a digital computer because it has only two digits—0 and 1. These two digits correspond to the two conditions under which transistors operate in a circuit—"on" or "off," depending upon the voltage level applied to them. Other number systems, such as *octal* (base 8) and *hexidecimal* (base 16), are also used in computers because they work well with the base 2 number system.

To help you to better understand the binary system, the following example of a counting device counting in the decimal (base 10) system is given.

At a professional football game an accurate count of the number of people in attendance is determined by having a counter connected to the turnstiles at each entrance to the stadium. As the first person passes through the turnstile, the counter changes from 0 to 1. As other people follow, the number on the counter advances until it reaches the number 9. At this point all of the digits (0–9) of the decimal number system have been used. As the next person passes through the turnstile, the first column of the counter goes from number 9 to 0, and the column to the left goes to 1. This is the number 10. The number 1 in the second column indicates that the digits in the first column have all been gone through once. When the number of persons passing through the turnstile reaches 20, the number 2 indicates that the numbers in the first column have been gone through twice.

The binary number system works in a similar fashion. However, since there are only two digits, 0 and 1, cycling through the digits is much quicker. For example, as with the base 10 system, when no one has passed through the turnstile, the counter reads 0000. After the first person passes through, the counter reads 0001. At this point all of the digits in the binary system have been used.

Just as in the base 10 system, when all the digits in the system have been used the first column is recycled back to 0, and the second column goes to 1 when the next person passes through the turnstile, Figure 3–1. The number looks just like the number 10 in the decimal system, but since only two people have passed through the turnstile, the quantity is really the same as a two in base 10. As the third person passes through the turnstile, the number in the first column changes to a 1, and the counter appears as shown in Figure 3–2. The number 1 in the second column indicates two people counted because both numbers in the first column have been cycled through. The number 1 in the first column indicates one additional person for a total of three. Since both columns are at 1, when the next person passes through the turnstile, the columns must both be recycled back to 0. The third column will then register a 1, as shown in Figure 3–3.

As you can see, the number 4 in the decimal system is 100 in binary. To

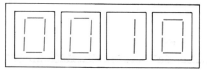

**Figure 3-1.** Binary counter after two people have passed through the gate.

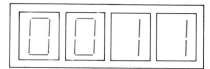

**Figure 3-2.** Binary counter after three people have passed through the gate.

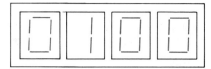

**Figure 3-3.** Binary counter after four people have passed through the gate.

avoid confusing binary numbers with decimal numbers, say the binary numbers as follows: 10 as one zero, 11 as one one, 100 as one zero zero, etc. Study Figure 3–4 carefully to learn how to count to 15 in the binary system. Practice counting various objects in binary rather than in the decimal number system to become familiar with the binary numerals from 0 to 15.

## Converting from Decimal to Binary

An easy method of converting from decimal to binary is illustrated in Figure 3–5. Given the decimal number 19, convert it to a binary number by dividing by 2 as many times as possible and recording the remainders from right to left. The remainders are 1, 1, 0, and 0. When the number is divided by 2 for the last time, record the quotient, which in this case is a 1, to the left of the remainders. The decimal number 19 is 10011 in binary.

Figure 3–6 illustrates another example of conversion from decimal to binary. The decimal number 22 is divided by 2 as many times as possible leaving remainders (from right to left) of 0, 1, 1, and 0 with a quotient of 1. The binary number 10110 is equal to the decimal number 22.

| DECIMAL | BINARY |
|:-------:|:------:|
| 0 | 0 |
| 1 | 1 |
| 2 | 10 |
| 3 | 11 |
| 4 | 100 |
| 5 | 101 |
| 6 | 110 |
| 7 | 111 |
| 8 | 1000 |
| 9 | 1001 |
| 10 | 1010 |
| 11 | 1011 |
| 12 | 1100 |
| 13 | 1101 |
| 14 | 1110 |
| 15 | 1111 |

**Figure 3-4.** Comparison of decimal and binary numbers

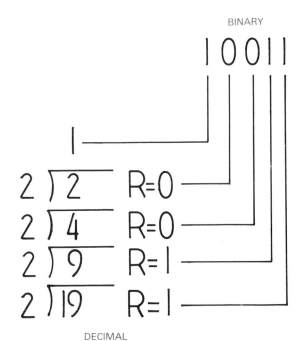

**Figure 3-5.** Converting a decimal number to a binary number

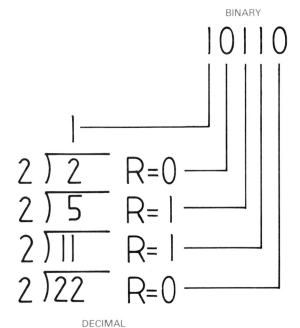

**Figure 3-6.** Another example of converting a decimal number to a binary number

### Converting from Binary to Decimal

Converting a large binary number to a decimal number by counting from zero is possible but very time-consuming. The following method of converting from decimal to binary is both easy and fast.

Figure 3-7 shows the place values in a binary number. As you read the values from right to left, you will observe that each value is twice the one to the right of it. For example, 16 is to the left of 8; 32 is to the left of 16; etc. These values are the powers of 2. To convert the binary number 0110 to a decimal number, use Figure 3-7 to find the place values of the digits in the number. Add the place values together to determine their sum (0 + 4 + 2 + 0), which is 6. In binary 0110 is equal to 6 in the decimal system.

In electronics, the place values of binary numbers are assigned to a row of lamps. Each lamp can be either on or off, indicating 1 or 0 in the binary number system, Figure 3-8. To determine the decimal number, the place values are added. Figure 3-9 illustrates the number 0101 in binary. The decimal value of this number is 5. Figure 3-10 shows the binary number 011011. To determine the decimal number equivalent, add the following place values: 1, 2, 8, and 16 to get the decimal number 27. If all of the lights are on, as in Figure 3-11, the binary number 111111 is shown. Add all of the numbers above the lights to convert the binary number to 63 in the decimal system. It is a good idea to learn to recognize any binary number between 0 and 15.

**THE OCTAL SYSTEM**

Because large numbers obviously get very lengthy in binary, other number systems that easily convert electronically to binary are used to program computers. One of these systems is the octal system.

The octal number system uses only eight digits (zero through 7), and then it recycles. That is to say, the octal system goes 0, 1, 2, 3, 4, 5, 6, 7, 10, 11, 12, 13, 14, 15, 16, 17, 20, etc. To convert an octal number to a binary number, simply convert each octal digit to its corresponding three-digit binary number and record it from left to right, Figure 3-12.

**Figure 3-7.** Place values in a binary number

● LAMP IS ON, INDICATING A 1

○ LAMP IS OFF, INDICATING A 0

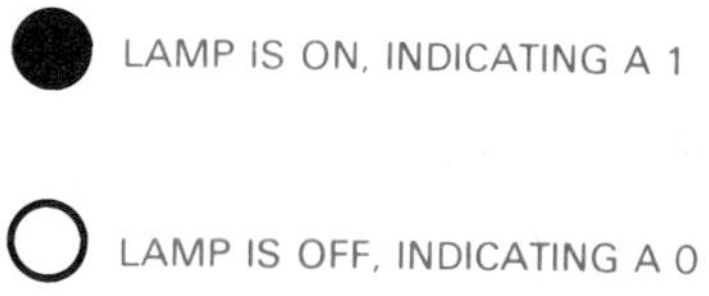

**Figure 3-8.** How lamps are used to display a binary number

### Numerical Control

A good example of the binary number system being used in industry is numerical control (NC). In NC systems a machine is programmed by means of a tape or card with holes punched in it. This coded information instructs the machine to operate in a certain way. For instance, a drill press can be instructed to drill a hole every four inches along a piece of metal.

Joseph Jacquard, a French inventor, developed a loom for weaving fabric based on the binary system nearly 200 years ago. Cards were punched with holes and then needles in the loom would feed thread through these holes to make patterns in the fabric. A hole in the card instructed the machine to weave; lack of a hole would instruct the machine not to weave. These two commands are comparable to the "on" and "off" of a digital electronic circuit.

Currently, many industries have begun to use machines programmed by computer numerical control (CNC). In this system, coded information is sent directly to the machine by a computer rather than through a card or tape. CNC offers greater speed and flexibility than traditional NC and is expected to become more widespread in the near future.

An NC tape reader being loaded. Coded information is contained in the punched tape (courtesy of Cincinnati Milacron, Inc.).

To convert a binary number to an octal number, reverse the process by dividing the binary number into groups of three. Then convert each group of three digits into a decimal digit, and record in order, Figure 3-13.

## THE HEXADECIMAL SYSTEM

Another very popular number system used in computers is the hexadecimal system. As its name indicates, "hex" equals six and "decimal" indicates 10, for a total of 16. This hexadecimal, or base 16, system is used in most personal computers. In hexadecimal you count from 0 to 9 as in the decimal system and then continue for six counts using the first six letters of the alphabet (A through F). Then, as in other systems, you recycle 10, 11, and so forth up through 1F and start over with 20, 21, etc.

As with the other number systems, it is important to be able to convert from hexadecimal to binary and from binary back to hexadecimal. For the hexadecimal numbers 0-F, it is helpful to know the binary equivalents or to refer to Figure 3-14. The process of conversion from hexadecimal to binary

**Figure 3-9.** Binary number 0101 displayed electronically

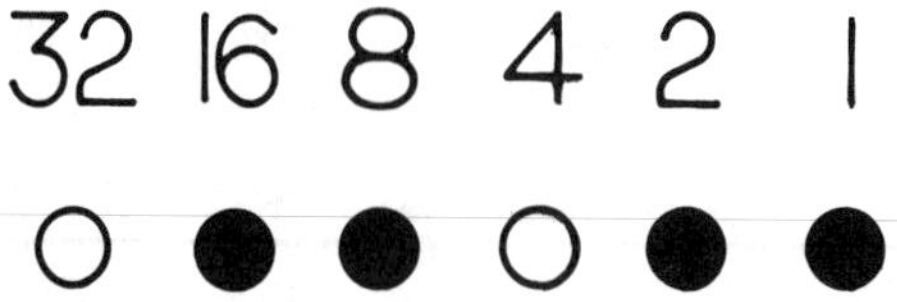

**Figure 3-10.** Binary number 011011 displayed electronically

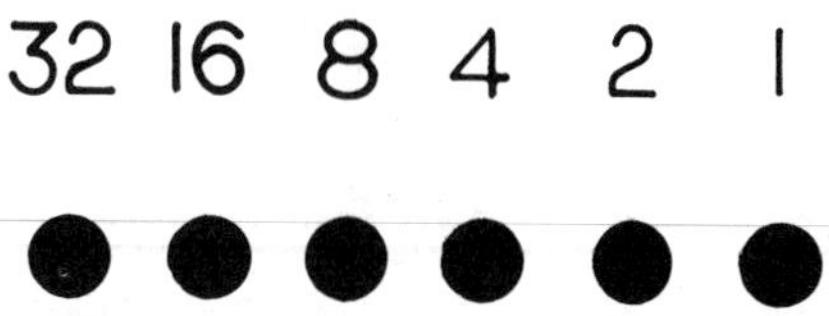

**Figure 3-11.** Binary number 111111 displayed electronically

is similar to the one used in converting from octal to binary except that each hexadecimal digit number or letter is broken down into four binary digits (1s or 0s), Figure 3-15. To convert back to hexadecimal from binary, the process is reversed. Simply divide a binary number into groups of four starting at the right, and change it into its hexadecimal equivalent, Figure 3-16. To convert a hexadecimal number to either octal or decimal numerals, simply convert it to binary and then to one of the other number systems.

As you will learn in future chapters, electronic circuits can rapidly convert a number system like binary to the decimal system. However, anyone who works with a digital computer should know how to convert from one number system to another in order to be able to check on the accuracy of the electronic circuits. The chart in Figure 3-17 will be helpful until you learn to count in the various number systems.

**Figure 3-12.** Converting an octal number to a binary number

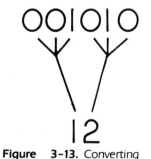

**Figure 3-13.** Converting a binary number to an octal number

| BINARY | HEXADECIMAL |
|--------|-------------|
| 0 | 0 |
| 1 | 1 |
| 10 | 2 |
| 11 | 3 |
| 100 | 4 |
| 101 | 5 |
| 110 | 6 |
| 111 | 7 |
| 1000 | 8 |
| 1001 | 9 |
| 1010 | A |
| 1011 | B |
| 1100 | C |
| 1101 | D |
| 1110 | E |
| 1111 | F |

**Figure 3-14.** Comparison of binary and hexadecimal numbers

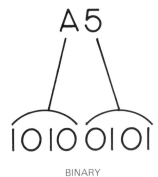

Figure 3-15. Converting from hexadecimal to binary

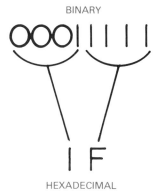

Figure 3-16. Converting from binary to hexadecimal

| DECIMAL | BINARY | OCTAL | HEXADECIMAL |
|---|---|---|---|
| 0 | 0 | 0 | 0 |
| 1 | 1 | 1 | 1 |
| 2 | 10 | 2 | 2 |
| 3 | 11 | 3 | 3 |
| 4 | 100 | 4 | 4 |
| 5 | 101 | 5 | 5 |
| 6 | 110 | 6 | 6 |
| 7 | 111 | 7 | 7 |
| 8 | 1000 | 10 | 8 |
| 9 | 1001 | 11 | 9 |
| 10 | 1010 | 12 | A |
| 11 | 1011 | 13 | B |
| 12 | 1100 | 14 | C |
| 13 | 1101 | 15 | D |
| 14 | 1110 | 16 | E |
| 15 | 1111 | 17 | F |

Figure 3-17. Comparison of number systems

**Figure 3-18.**    *Lamps indicating binary numbers*

**SUMMARY**          Digital electronics uses the binary number system because the 1 and 0 of the number system correspond to the on and off of a circuit. Other number systems such as octal and hexadecimal are also useful because their numbers can easily be converted to binary and vice versa. It will be easier to learn digital electronics if you know the binary number system. You should also be able to apply the rules given in this chapter for converting from binary to decimal, octal, and hexadecimal, and for converting from those systems back to binary.

## REVIEW QUESTIONS

1. In a binary number, each value is _____ the value of the number to the _____.
2. If the lamps that are on indicate a binary 1, and the lamps that are off indicate a binary 0, record the proper decimal for each set of lamps in Figure 3-18.
3. Convert the following decimal numbers to binary numbers: 7, 12.
4. Convert the following binary numbers to decimal numbers: 0101, 1001.
5. Convert the following binary numbers to octal numbers: 1000, 1101.
6. Convert the following octal numbers to binary numbers: 6, 10.
7. Convert the following hexadecimal numbers to binary numbers: A3, 1E.

## SUGGESTED ACTIVITIES

Make a calendar of the next month in binary. At the end of each day, cross it off the calendar.

# DIGITAL LOGIC GATES

# 4

## OBJECTIVES

After studying this chapter, you will be able to:
- Identify digital logic gates by interpreting their letter makeup.
- Understand the operation of several common logic gates.
- Use truth tables to determine information about logic gates.

## OVERVIEW

In order to work with the various number systems, digital computers use tiny circuits built into silicon chips. These circuits are called logic gates. In this chapter you will learn about basic logic gates and study their truth tables and their symbols.

**IDENTIFYING
LOGIC GATES**

Electronic circuits used for digital logic are called logic gates. They are made up of transistors, diodes, resistors, or a combination of these. These circuits are essential parts of computers and other electronic devices such as timers, music synthesizers, digital clocks, etc. The types of logic gates are identified by the first letters of their main components. The most common type of digital logic circuit, the *TTL* (transistor-transistor logic), is composed of transistors. Figure 4–1 is an example of a transistor-transistor logic circuit.

Another example of a digital logic circuit is the *DTL* (diode-transistor logic). The main components of the DTL are the diode and transistor. Figure 4–2 illustrates a diode-transistor logic circuit.

**FAMILIES OF ICS**

A group of ICs distinguishable by its major components (such as the TTL) is referred to as a family. The TTL group is one of the most popular types of families. For convenience, this family has been assigned the

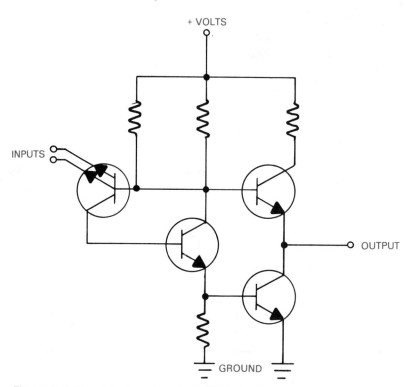

**Figure 4–1.** *Transistor-transistor logic (TTL) circuit*

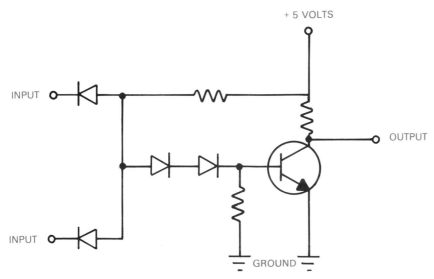

**Figure 4-2.** Diode-transistor logic (DTL) circuit

number 74XX. The 74XX means that this group includes numbers 7400, 7401, 7402, etc. The 74XX ICs use more current than any other family of ICs, and high current creates heat. Therefore, the circuits have to be relatively large compared to those of other ICs in order to keep the transistors from being damaged by heat.

A family of ICs that uses less current is the *MOS* (metal-oxide semiconductors) group. These ICs can have more components in a smaller area than the TTL-type ICs. Transistors on MOS-type ICs are usually *FET* (field effect transistors), which are voltage-controlled rather than current-controlled. Because they are voltage-controlled, the amount of current they use is much less than TTL ICs. The fact that they use less current means that less heat is created, and more components can be built into a smaller space.

There are many types of MOS ICs. One type is *CMOS* (complementary metal-oxide semiconductor). Many, but not all, of the same types of circuits found in the TTL 74XX family of ICs are available in the 4000 series (CMOS ICs). CMOS ICs are used in some small battery-operated devices because of their low current drain. Because they operate more slowly than TTL ICs, CMOS ICs are limited to low-speed circuits. Another disadvantage of CMOS in comparison to TTL ICs is that they can be easily damaged by static electricity. In order to avoid damage, CMOS ICs must be carefully handled:

- As with all ICs, power should be off when removing or installing.
- CMOS ICs should be stored in either conductive foam or aluminum foil because these materials do not build up a charge of static electricity. Do not store CMOS ICs in styrofoam because it takes on a static charge very easily.
- All equipment such as soldering pencils and test equipment should be properly grounded.

## VOLTAGE LEVELS

The components that make up a logic gate are controlled (caused to conduct or not to conduct) by proper voltage levels being applied to them. The voltage used is DC voltage. There are only two voltage levels needed— approximately 5 volts and almost no volts at all. The two voltage levels are referred to as *high* and *low*. Five volts is high voltage and close to zero voltage is low voltage. The high voltage affects logic gates in a manner opposite to that of the low voltage. Figure 4–3 shows a graph with high and low voltage levels.

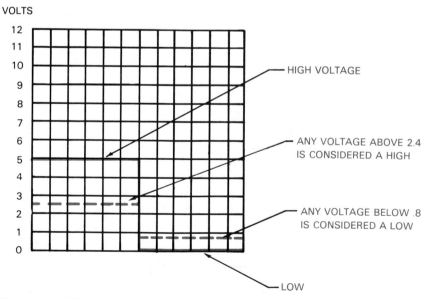

**Figure 4–3.** High and low voltage levels for logic circuits

VOLTS

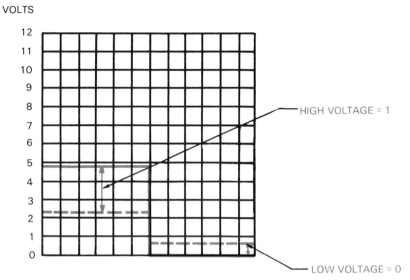

**Figure 4-4.** High voltage represents 1 and low voltage represents 0.

In Chapter 3 you learned that there are only two digits or numbers in the binary number system-1s and 0s. Not only do these two digits correspond to on and off in a circuit, but they are also related to the voltage levels high and low. The high voltage is referred to as number 1, and the low voltage is referred to as 0, Figure 4-4.

There can be one or more inputs to a logic gate, but there is only one output per gate. The inputs are voltages (high or low) from an external source. The output of the gate is low or high depending upon whether the transistor that controls it is conducting or not. The output of a logic gate can be thought of as a light that can only be off, as in Figure 4-5A, or on as in Figure 4-5B.

**INPUTS AND OUTPUTS**

If the transistor that controls the output is caused to fully conduct by a combination of inputs, the voltage drop across it is very low (less than .8 volt or a 0), Figure 4-6. On the other hand, if the combination of inputs to a logic gate is such that the transistor does not conduct, the voltage across it is high (approximately 5 volts or a 1), Figure 4-7. The two states of the output of a logic gate are also referred to as high and low, depending upon the amount of voltage that is present.

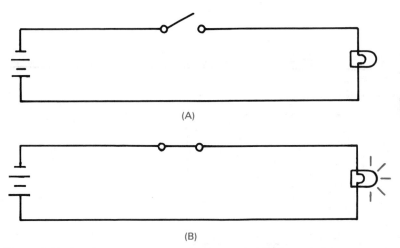

**Figure 4-5.** Circuit showing two possible states. In (A), the switch is open and the light is off. In (B), the switch is closed and the light is on.

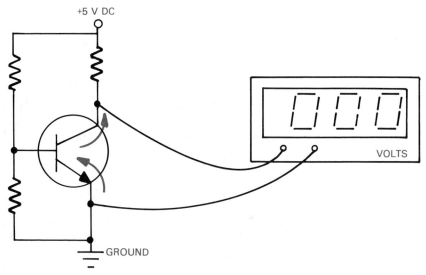

**Figure 4-6.** Voltmeter connected across a transistor that is conducting indicates a low (or 0) output. Arrows show the direction of current flow.

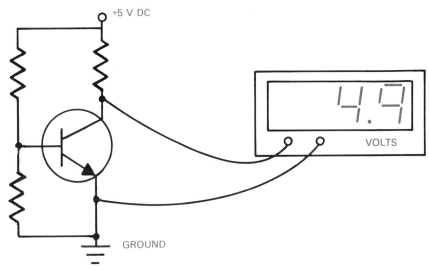

**Figure 4-7.** Voltmeter connected across a transistor that is not conducting indicates a high (or 1) output.

Logic gates are used for making decisions. Because there are only two choices that a logic gate can make (output high or low), its operation is fairly simple. By connecting a number of them together, however, logic gates can handle complex problems.

**OPERATION OF LOGIC GATES**

A good example of a logic gate is the *AND* gate. Its name indicates something about how it operates. For example, if it has two inputs labeled A and B, both inputs A and B must be high to make the output high. The operation of an AND gate can be compared to the circuit shown in Figure 4-8. In the circuit, only when switch A and switch B are closed (on position)

**AND GATE**

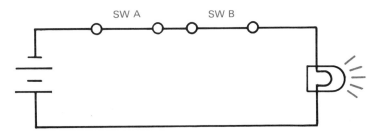

**Figure 4-8.** Two switches in series with a lamp. Both switches must be in closed position in order to light the lamp.

will the light bulb be on (high output). If either switch A or switch B or both are open (off position), the light bulb is off (low output), Figure 4–9.

A practical application of an electrical circuit that operates similar to an AND gate is the power-operated paper cutter in a print shop. To prevent the possibility of the operator's hand being under the blade when the paper is cut, the machine is designed with two pushbutton switches placed on opposite sides of the machine away from the blade. Both switches must be held in to make the blade operate, Figure 4–10. When the blade completes its cut, the operator can release the switches.

The symbol for a digital logic AND gate is shown in Figure 4–11. Become familiar with it and the other logic gate symbols, because they will be used in other diagrams you will study.

Figure 4–12 shows a two-input AND gate with all of the possible input combinations and their outputs. AND gates can have more than two inputs, but all of the inputs must be 1s for the output to be a 1. If even one of the inputs is a 0, then the output will be a 0. The operation of an AND gate may be compared to the decision-making of the United Nations Security Council. The Council has five permanent member countries, each having one representative. In order for the Council to pass any resolution, all five countries must agree to it. If even one country votes differently from the rest, the resolution does not pass. Because AND gates operate this way, they are sometimes called "all or nothing" gates.

## TRUTH TABLES

A *truth table* is a chart that lists the output for each possible combination of inputs. The letters used to label the inputs on a truth table are placed in order from right to left. This is so that if more inputs are added the letters are still in alphabetical order.

Truth tables are very helpful to anyone working in digital electronics. Instead of making all of the electronic connections to a logic gate to determine the output for a particular combination of inputs, the information can be found in the truth table. For example, by looking at the truth table for an AND gate in Figure 4–13, you can see that if input A is a 1 (high) and input B is a 0 (low), the output will be a 0 (low).

A second important feature of the truth table is that the possible combinations of inputs are listed in binary order from 0000 to 1111 (zero to fifteen in the decimal system). This listing method makes it easier to check to see that none of the possible combinations are missed. Figure 4–14 shows a truth table with the possible combinations of inputs listed in binary order for a four-input AND gate. The symbol for a four-input AND gate is shown in Figure 4–15.

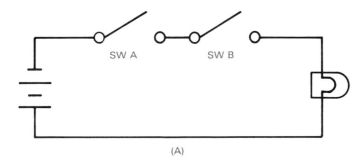

(A)

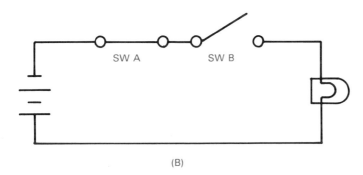

(B)

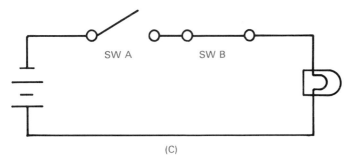

(C)

**Figure 4-9.** Circuits with two switches in series and at least one switch open. In each case, the lamp cannot light.

**Figure 4-10.** Paper cutter with two controls. Both must be pushed at the same time in order to operate the machine.

**Figure 4-11.** Symbol for a digital logic AND gate

Figure 4-12. Two-input AND gate showing all possible combinations of inputs and outputs

Figure 4-13. Truth table for an AND gate

| INPUTS | | | | OUTPUT |
|---|---|---|---|---|
| D | C | B | A | X |
| 0 | 0 | 0 | 0 | 0 |
| 0 | 0 | 0 | 1 | 0 |
| 0 | 0 | 1 | 0 | 0 |
| 0 | 0 | 1 | 1 | 0 |
| 0 | 1 | 0 | 0 | 0 |
| 0 | 1 | 0 | 1 | 0 |
| 0 | 1 | 1 | 0 | 0 |
| 0 | 1 | 1 | 1 | 0 |
| 1 | 0 | 0 | 0 | 0 |
| 1 | 0 | 0 | 1 | 0 |
| 1 | 0 | 1 | 0 | 0 |
| 1 | 0 | 1 | 1 | 0 |
| 1 | 1 | 0 | 0 | 0 |
| 1 | 1 | 0 | 1 | 0 |
| 1 | 1 | 1 | 0 | 0 |
| 1 | 1 | 1 | 1 | 1 |

**Figure 4-14.** Truth table for a four-input AND gate

INPUT A
INPUT B
INPUT C
INPUT D

OUTPUT X

**Figure 4-15.** Symbol for a four-input AND gate

When engineers develop truth tables for the various types of logic gates, they use a special kind of mathematics called *Boolean algebra*. Although Boolean algebra originated many years ago from the thinking of George Boole, there was very little use for it until recently, when digital electronics was developed.

By using Boolean algebraic statements or laws, the output of a logic gate can be determined if the inputs are known. The Boolean statement that applies to an AND gate is $A \cdot B = X$, Figure 4-16. The capital letters A, B, and X are symbols that indicate the value of 1 or a logic high. The multiplication symbol ($\cdot$) means and. In this case A·B means A and B or, more correctly, both A and B. The equal sign (=) separates the input symbols from the output symbol in the statement. Thus, this statement says that if A and B (inputs) are both 1s, then X (output) must also be 1.

**LOGIC GATES AND MATH**

In practical application, several logic gates are contained in an integrated circuit. The chip is processed so that the numerous components such as transistors, diodes, resistors, etc., are included as needed to form the desired logic gates. The body of the IC is made of a plastic material that surrounds the silicon chip, protecting it from damage, Figure 4-17.

**PACKAGING LOGIC GATES**

Input and output connections from the logic gates within the silicon chip are made to pins that are extended from the body of the IC, as in Figure 4-18. A diagram, like Figure 4-19, that allows you to see what each of these

**PIN-OUT**

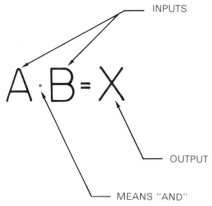

**Figure 4-16.** Boolean statement for an AND gate

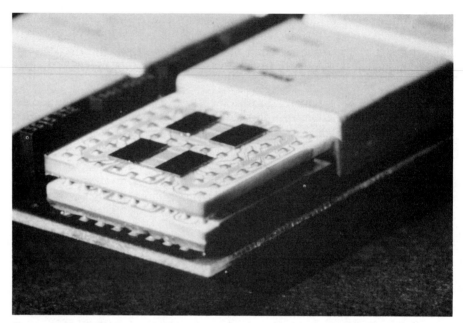

**Figure 4-17.** Plastic case surrounding a silicon chip (courtesy of IBM Corporation)

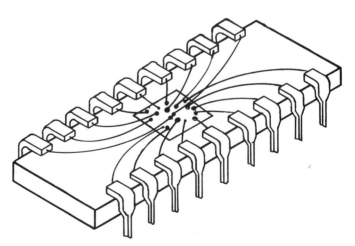

**Figure 4-18.** A diagram showing connections from the silicon chip of the IC to its external pins

pins of the IC is connected to is known as a *pin-out* diagram. Pin-out is a term used to describe the connections made.

Figure 4–19 illustrates a *quad* two-input AND gate which is identified by the number 7408. This IC contains four (quad) individual AND gates, and each gate has two inputs. The positive 5 volts DC needed to power the IC is connected through pin 14; the negative side of the power supply is connected through pin 7. (The ground symbol usually indicates negative.) You can see in this diagram that pins 1 and 2 are connected to the inputs of one of the AND gates, and pin 3 is connected to the output of that same gate.

**OR GATE**

Another common logic gate is the *OR* gate. Like the AND gate, its name indicates something about how it operates. If an OR gate has two inputs, labeled A and B, if either A or B is high or if both A and B are high, the output is high. Only when both inputs are lows is the output a low.

The operation of the OR gate can be compared to two switches in parallel with each other connected to a lamp, as in Figure 4–20. If either one or both of the switches are in the closed position (on—corresponding to high or 1 output), then the light bulb would be on (high output). Only when both switches are in the open position (off—corresponding to low or 0 input) would the light be off. Just as the term *and* indicates the operation of AND gates, the term *or* also indicates an operation. In this example, if either

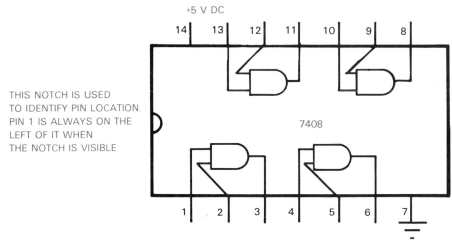

**Figure 4-19.** Pin-out diagram of an IC

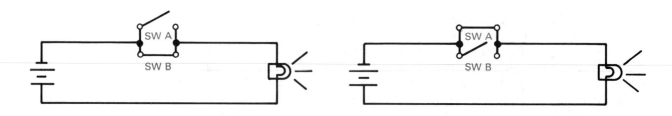

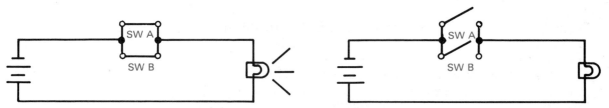

**Figure 4-20.** An OR gate operates much like two switches in parallel.

switch A or switch B or both A and B are closed, the light is on. The symbol and truth table for an OR gate appear in Figure 4-21.

The Boolean statement that applies to the OR gate is A + B = X, Figure 4-22. A and B can again be used to indicate high or 1 inputs and X as a 1 output. The plus sign (+) means or, and the equal sign (=) again separates the inputs from the outputs. Thus, the statement A + B = X says that when input A or input B or both A and B are 1s, then the output X is a 1. It is important to remember that a (+) sign means *or* and that a (·) means *and*. Figure 4-23 diagrams the pin-out of a quad two-input OR gate IC. This IC is identified by the number 7432.

## INVERTER

The next gate you will learn about is probably the easiest to remember because it is the simplest. The *inverter* has only one input and, like all logic gates, only one output. It does what its name implies, and that is to invert or change the input to an output of the opposite state, Figure 4-24. For example, if the input is a 1, then the output is a 0. If the input is a 0, then the output is a 1.

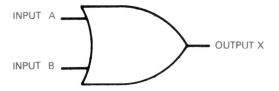

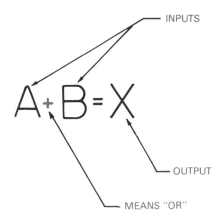

**Figure 4-22.** Boolean statement for an OR gate

| INPUTS | | OUTPUT |
|--------|--------|--------|
| B | A | X |
| 0 | 0 | 0 |
| 0 | 1 | 1 |
| 1 | 0 | 1 |
| 1 | 1 | 1 |

**Figure 4-21.** Symbol and truth table for an OR gate

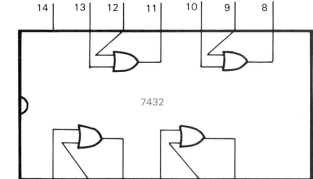

**Figure 4-23.** Pin-out diagram of a quad two-input OR gate IC

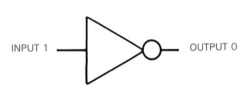

| INPUT | OUTPUT |
|-------|--------|
| A | X |
| 0 | 1 |
| 1 | 0 |

**Figure 4-24.** Diagrams of an inverter showing that output is always opposite of input

**Figure 4-25.** Symbol and truth table for an inverter

The symbol and truth table for an inverter appear in Figure 4-25. The truth table for the inverter is always the same as that shown in the figure because there can be only one input, and it can have only two possible states—1 or 0.

The Boolean statement for an inverter is $A = \overline{A}$, Figure 4-26. A is the input, and $\overline{A}$ is the output. The line above the second A means *not* (in this case, not A). In other words, whatever input A is (either 1 or 0), then the output is "not." The inverter is sometimes called the NOT gate because it does not make decisions dependent upon the combination of inputs as the OR and AND gates do. It simply changes the input to the opposite state at the output. Figure 4-27 diagrams the pin-out of IC number 7404. This IC is called a hex inverter because it contains six (hex) inverter gates.

The AND gate, the OR gate, and the inverter are the three basic logic gates. Other gates you will learn about are modifications of these three.

## NAND GATE

A NAND gate is made by inverting the output of an AND gate. Figure 4-28 shows an AND gate with an inverter connected so as to operate as a NAND gate. Since the output of an AND gate is inverted to make a NAND gate, the output of a NAND gate is always opposite that of an AND gate for

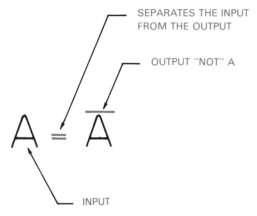

**Figure 4-26.** Boolean statement for an inverter

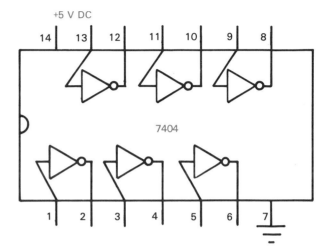

**Figure 4-27.** Pin-out diagram of a hex inverter IC

the same combinations of inputs. For example, only when you have both inputs of a two-input AND gate high do you get a high output; with a NAND gate, when both inputs are high, you get a low output.

Compare the truth table for a NAND gate to that of an AND gate and you will see that the NAND gate operates exactly opposite an AND gate, Figure 4-29. Figure 4-30 shows that the symbol for a NAND gate is the same as that for an AND gate except for the small circle at the output of the gate. This small circle indicates that a NAND gate inverts the output of the AND gate. Remember that an inverter gate is also called a NOT gate. Since a NAND gate is just an inverted AND gate, it could be called a NOT AND gate, but this has been shortened to just NAND.

The Boolean statement for a NAND gate is $\overline{A \cdot B} = X$, Figure 4-31. Remember that the times symbol (·) means *and* and that A and B are considered 1s. In this statement, the line over A and B means not. If both A and B are 0, the X is a 1. In fact, the only time X is 0 is when A and B are both 1.

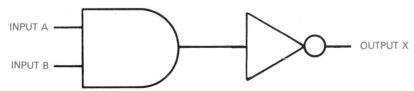

**Figure 4-28.** NAND gate made by inverting the output of an AND gate

# AND                                     NAND

| INPUTS | | OUTPUT |
|---|---|---|
| B | A | X |
| 0 | 0 | 0 |
| 0 | 1 | 0 |
| 1 | 0 | 0 |
| 1 | 1 | 1 |

| INPUTS | | OUTPUT |
|---|---|---|
| B | A | X |
| 0 | 0 | 1 |
| 0 | 1 | 1 |
| 1 | 0 | 1 |
| 1 | 1 | 0 |

**Figure 4-29.** Comparison of AND gate and NAND gate truth tables

Figure 4-32 diagrams the pin-out of a quad two-input NAND gate IC. This IC is identified by the number 7400. As you will see in later chapters, NAND can be used in many different ways and is thus a very popular gate.

**NOR GATE**     As you have probably already guessed, a *NOR* gate is simply an OR gate whose output has been inverted. The diagram of an OR gate and inverter in Figure 4-33 shows the function of a NOR gate. With a two-input OR gate, only if both inputs are 0 will the output be 0. With a two-input NOR gate, only when both inputs are 0 do you get a 1 as the output.

The NOR gate gets its name in the same way that the NAND gate does; that is, because its function is "not" OR (not means opposite to, or inverted), NOT OR has been abbreviated to NOR. The truth table for a NOR gate appears in Figure 4-34. The symbol for a NOR gate is the same as that for an OR gate except for the small circle at the output which means invert, Figure 4-35.

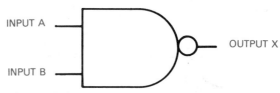

INPUT A

OUTPUT X

INPUT B

**Figure 4-30.** Symbol for a NAND gate

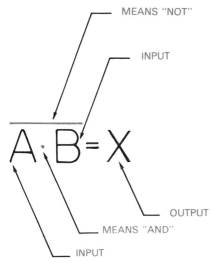

**Figure 4-31.** Boolean statement for a NAND gate

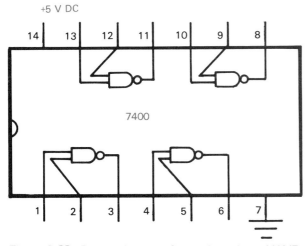

**Figure 4-32.** Pin-out diagram of a quad two-input NAND gate IC

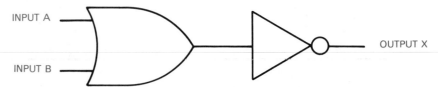

**Figure 4-33.** NOR gate made by inverting the output of an OR gate

The Boolean statement for a NOR gate is $\overline{A + B} = X$. Remember that the plus sign (+) means or, and the line above A + B means A or B "not." In this statement, X output is 0 only if neither A nor B are 1s (not A or B).

The diagram in Figure 4-36 shows the layout of a quad two-input NOR gate. This IC is identified by the number 7402.

If you remember the functions of AND, OR, and inverters, you can figure out the NAND and NOR functions. Simply invert the output of an AND to get the NAND function; invert the output of an OR to get the NOR function. Until you can remember the truth tables for each gate, refer to Figure 4-37.

**SUMMARY**          Logic gates are tiny circuits built into ICs. The output of each type of gate depends upon its makeup and the inputs that are applied to it. To determine the function of a gate without experimenting, you can study the truth table for the gate. A Boolean statement describing the function is also available for each type of gate. For each of the popular two-input gates, it is a

| INPUTS | | OUTPUT |
|---|---|---|
| B | A | X |
| 0 | 0 | 1 |
| 0 | 1 | 0 |
| 1 | 0 | 0 |
| 1 | 1 | 0 |

**Figure 4-34.** Truth table for a NOR gate

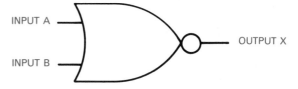

**Figure 4-35.** Symbol for a NOR gate

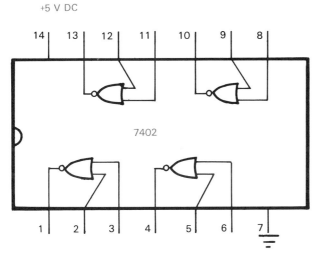

+5 V DC

7402

**Figure 4-36.** Pin-out diagram of a quad two-input NOR gate IC

good idea to know the output you can expect from each combination of inputs. When actually building circuits with digital logic ICs, you will use pin-out diagrams. These diagrams show the location of all connections necessary for each IC.

## REVIEW QUESTIONS

1. Circuits used in digital electronics are called _____.
2. The type of digital logic that uses transistors as the main components is called _____ logic.
3. Select the best answer: The binary digit 1 in digital electronics means (a) a low, (b) a high, (c) neither low nor high.
4. Select the best answer: If the output of a two-input AND gate is high, the inputs are (a) both low, (b) both high, (c) A high; B low, (d) A low; B high.
5. Explain how logic gates can be made to handle complex problems.
6. Select the best answer: If the output of a two-input OR gate is low, the inputs are (a) both low, (b) both high, (c) A high; B low, (d) A low; B high.
7. Explain why the binary number system is used in digital electronics.

| SYMBOL | INPUTS | | OUTPUT |
|---|---|---|---|
| | B | A | X |
| 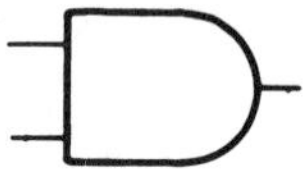 AND | 0 | 0 | 0 |
| | 0 | 1 | 0 |
| | 1 | 0 | 0 |
| | 1 | 1 | 1 |
| 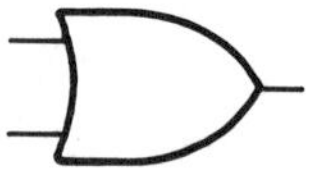 OR | 0 | 0 | 0 |
| | 0 | 1 | 1 |
| | 1 | 0 | 1 |
| | 1 | 1 | 1 |
| 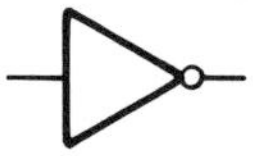 INVERTER | | 1 | 0 |
| | | 0 | 1 |
| 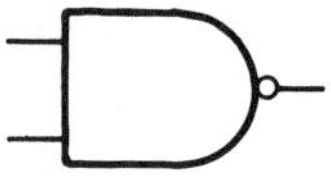 NAND | 0 | 0 | 1 |
| | 0 | 1 | 1 |
| | 1 | 0 | 1 |
| | 1 | 1 | 0 |
| 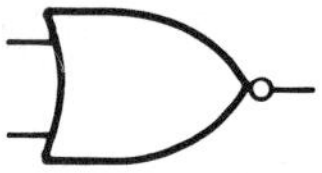 NOR | 0 | 0 | 1 |
| | 0 | 1 | 0 |
| | 1 | 0 | 0 |
| | 1 | 1 | 0 |

**Figure 4-37.** Truth table for basic logic gates

8. If one input of a NAND gate is high, and the other is low, the output will be _____.
9. Explain the function of an inverter.
10. The following truth table is for the _____ gate.

| B | A | X |
|---|---|---|
| 0 | 0 | 1 |
| 0 | 1 | 0 |
| 1 | 0 | 0 |
| 1 | 1 | 0 |

# SUGGESTED ACTIVITIES

1. Make a truth table for a four-input NAND gate. Show all of the possible input combinations and the correct output.
2. List the pins to which the positive and negative terminals of the power supply would be connected on a 7408 quad two-input AND gate IC.
3. List the pins that are connected to the outputs of the four OR gates in a 7432 quad two-input OR gate IC.
4. Using the symbols for an AND gate and an inverter, make a diagram of a circuit that would function the same as a NAND gate.
5. Using two single-pole single-throw switches, a battery, a lamp, and some electrical hook-up wire, wire a circuit that will demonstrate how a two-input AND gate works. (Be sure to consult your instructor first and to follow safety procedures to avoid shock.)
6. Rewire the circuit in Number 5 to demonstrate how an OR gate works.

## ALTERNATE SUGGESTED ACTIVITIES

1. Wire the circuit shown in Figure 4–38 on a solderless breadboard. (Do not connect the power until told to do so.) Check all connections for wiring errors.
2. Use a well-filtered power supply or batteries connected to provide about 5 volts DC. Connect the positive side of the power supply to Pin 14 of the 7408 and the negative side to Pin 7.
3. Does the LED light? Notice that both inputs (Pins 1 and 2) of the AND gate are connected to 5 volts.

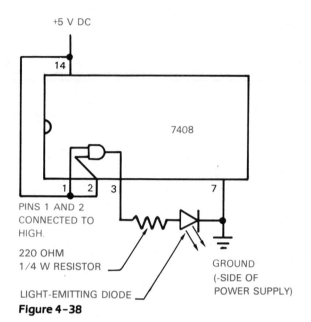

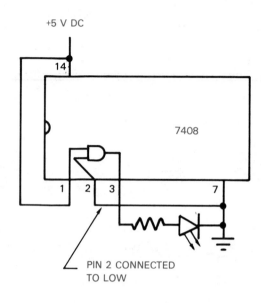

**Figure 4-38**

4. Disconnect the power supply. Rewire the circuit as shown in Figure 4–38.
5. Reconnect the power supply. Does the LED light? Does this prove that the truth table for an AND gate is correct?
6. Disconnect the power supply and carefully put away all components and equipment used in this experiment.

# 5

# COMBINING LOGIC GATES TO MAKE OTHER GATES

## OBJECTIVES

After studying this chapter, you will be able to:
- Use logic gates as building blocks to make circuits that function as a particular logic gate.
- Explain why the NAND gate is called the universal gate.

## OVERVIEW

In many cases an integrated circuit package contains four or more logic gates. Frequently only one or two of the gates need to be used, and the others are surplus in that particular integrated circuit (IC). These readily available surplus gates may be combined to perform the function of some other gate when it is needed. Such combinations can save considerable expense, especially if thousands of boards are going to be produced. Combining can also save space on the circuit board, thus making it possible to build a smaller product. In this chapter you will learn how to make needed gates by combining gates or by using the NAND gate as a universal gate.

## MAKING AN AND GATE

An easy way to make an AND gate is to use two inverters and a NOR gate, as shown in Figure 5-1. By using all of the possible combinations of inputs to the circuit, you get a truth table that looks like the one in Figure 5-2.

Starting with 0s at both inputs, the inverters will make both inputs to the NOR gate 1's. If both inputs to a NOR gate are 1's, the output will be a 0. Change input A to a 1, and leave input B at 0. The inverters will make the inputs to the NOR gate a 1 and a 0, which will still give a 0 output. Only when both inputs are 1's, as in the last combination of inputs in the truth table, will the inverters make the inputs to the NOR gate both 0s. If both inputs to a NOR gate are 0s, the output will be a 1.

## MAKING AN OR GATE

If an AND gate can be made by inverting the inputs to a NOR gate, it is worth investigating the possibility of inverting the inputs to a NAND gate to make an OR gate. Figure 5-3 shows a NAND gate with its inputs inverted. Figure 5-4 shows the truth table derived from that circuit. The accuracy of the truth table can be checked by using all of the possible combinations of inputs to the circuit. With both inputs A and B at 0, the inputs to the NAND gates will both be 1's. If both inputs to a NAND gate are 1's, the output will be 0. Change input A to a 1, and leave input B at 0. The inputs to the NAND gate will now be 0 and 1. With the inputs to a NAND gate being 0 and 1, the output will be a 1. The next combination of inputs (A = 0, B = 1) will give the same result. The last combination of inputs, which is a 1 at both A and B, will create a 0 at both inputs of the NAND gate and produce an output of 1. Checking all of the combinations will prove that inverting the input to a NAND gate will make an OR gate.

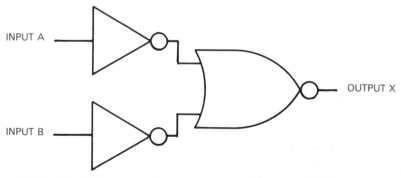

INPUT A

INPUT B

OUTPUT X

**Figure 5-1.** AND gate made by inverting the inputs to a NOR gate

| INPUTS | | OUTPUT |
|---|---|---|
| B | A | X |
| 0 | 0 | 0 |
| 0 | 1 | 0 |
| 1 | 0 | 0 |
| 1 | 1 | 1 |

**Figure 5-2.** Truth table for an AND gate made by inverting the inputs of a NOR gate

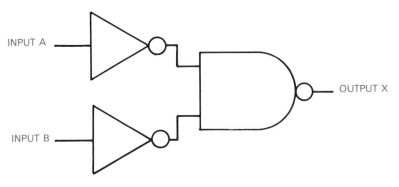

**Figure 5-3.** OR gate made by inverting the inputs of a NAND gate

You can make a NOR gate by simply inverting the inputs to an AND **MAKING A NOR GATE**
gate. Figure 5-5 shows the circuit that will give you the same truth table as
that of a NOR gate. The truth table for the circuit in Figure 5-5 is shown in
Figure 5-6.

By putting a 0 at both inputs A and B of the circuit in Figure 5-5, you
get 1's at both inputs to the AND gate. The output of an AND gate whose
inputs are both 1 is a 1. Next, make input A = 1 and input B = 0. After being
inverted, the inputs to the AND gate will be 0 and 1, and the output will be 0.
If you reverse the 1 and 0 at inputs A and B, the result will be the same—a 0.
Finally, if both inputs A and B are 1's, then you find 0's at both inputs of the
AND gate and a 0 at the output. Compare the truth table in Figure 5-6 to the
truth table for a NOR gate (Figure 4-34).

| INPUTS | | OUTPUT |
|---|---|---|
| B | A | X |
| 0 | 0 | 0 |
| 0 | 1 | 1 |
| 1 | 0 | 1 |
| 1 | 1 | 1 |

**Figure 5-4.** Truth table for an
OR gate made by inverting the
inputs of a NAND gate

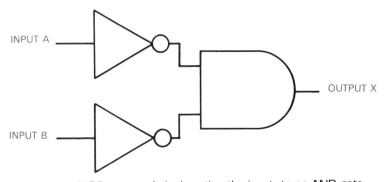

**Figure 5-5.** NOR gate made by inverting the inputs to an AND gate

| INPUTS | | OUTPUT |
|---|---|---|
| B | A | X |
| 0 | 0 | 1 |
| 0 | 1 | 0 |
| 1 | 0 | 0 |
| 1 | 1 | 0 |

**Figure 5-6.** Truth table for a NOR gate made by inverting the inputs to an AND gate

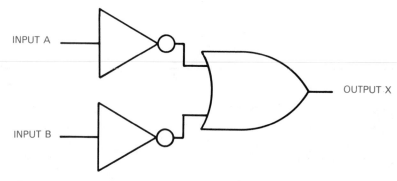

**Figure 5-7.** NAND gate made by inverting the inputs to an OR gate

## MAKING A NAND GATE

Figure 5-7 shows how you can connect two inverters to the inputs of an OR gate to make a circuit that functions as a NAND gate. By following through the truth table in Figure 5-8, you can see that the output is the same as the truth table for a NAND gate.

Start as usual with 0's to both inputs. The inverters will change these 0's to 1's. With both inputs to an OR gate as 1's, the output will be a 1. Next, make input A a 1 and input B a 0. Doing this will make the inputs to the OR gate a 0 and a 1, which will give an output of 1. The next input of 0 at input A and 1 at input B will produce the same results as the inputs that were just

| INPUTS | | OUTPUT |
|---|---|---|
| B | A | X |
| 0 | 0 | 1 |
| 0 | 1 | 1 |
| 1 | 0 | 1 |
| 1 | 1 | 0 |

**Figure 5-8.** Truth table for a NAND gate made by inverting the inputs to an OR gate

used because both A and B inputs are connected through the same kind of gate (inverter) to the inputs of an OR gate. Finally, with a 1 to both inputs A and B, the inverter will make the inputs to the OR gate both 0s. When both inputs of an OR gate are 0s, the output is also 0. Compare the output of this circuit to that of a NAND gate, and you will find that they are the same.

A very easy and inexpensive way of making an inverter is to connect the inputs of either a NAND or NOR gate together. By connecting the inputs, you reduce the input to one, just as in an inverter. The output, as you can see in the modified truth table in Figure 5-9, is always opposite the input, just as in an inverter. For example, by connecting the inputs of a two-input NAND gate together, you can make a gate that functions just like an inverter. If a 1 is put to the junction of the two inputs, then with both inputs to NAND gate 1's, the output is 0. On the other hand, if a 0 is put to the

**MAKING INVERTERS FROM NAND AND NOR GATES**

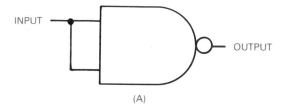

(A)

| INPUT | OUTPUT |
|---|---|
| A | X |
| 0 | 1 |
| 1 | 0 |

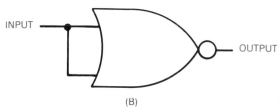

(B)

**Figure 5-9.** How a NAND gate (A) or a NOR gate (B) may be connected to function as an inverter. Truth table for an inverter is also shown.

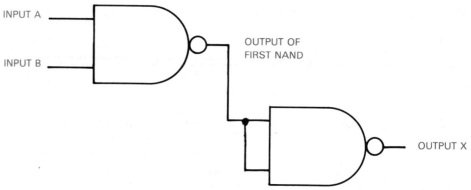

**Figure 5-10.** AND gate made from two NAND gates

junction of the two inputs, wherever both inputs to a NAND gate are 0, the output is 1. Since inverters are used a great deal in digital electronics, it is important to know this method of making an inverter when extra NAND or NOR gates are available.

## NAND AS A UNIVERSAL GATE

Any of the gates that you have learned about so far can be made from the right combination of NAND gates. Figure 5-10 illustrates using only NAND gates to make an AND gate. Since the output of a NAND gate is the opposite of an AND, the second NAND gate is used to invert the output of the first, which gives the truth table in Figure 5-11. The output of this table is the same as that of an AND gate.

| INPUTS | | OUTPUT OF NAND | OUTPUT |
|---|---|---|---|
| B | A | | X |
| 0 | 0 | 1 | 0 |
| 0 | 1 | 1 | 0 |
| 1 | 0 | 1 | 0 |
| 1 | 1 | 0 | 1 |

**Figure 5-11.** Truth table for an AND gate made from two NAND gates

| INPUTS | | INPUTS TO THE LAST NAND GATE | | OUTPUT |
|---|---|---|---|---|
| B | A | | | X |
| 0 | 0 | 1 | 1 | 0 |
| 0 | 1 | 1 | 0 | 1 |
| 1 | 0 | 0 | 1 | 1 |
| 1 | 1 | 0 | 0 | 1 |

**Figure 5-12.** Truth table for an OR gate made from NAND gates

To make an OR gate using only NAND gates, simply use NAND gates as inverters to invert both inputs to a NAND gate. The output of the truth table for this connection will be the same as the truth table of an OR gate, Figure 5-12. Only one more gate would be needed to make the circuit in Figure 5-12 function as a NOR gate rather than an OR. By inverting the output, the circuit would function as a NOR gate.

A NAND gate is used as an inverter to make the circuit of Figure 5-13. Figure 5-14 shows the truth table for this circuit. The output of the truth table for this circuit has the same output as that of the truth table of a NOR gate.

Although using two, three, or four gates to replace one gate may not always be convenient, there are some cases where buying large quantities of

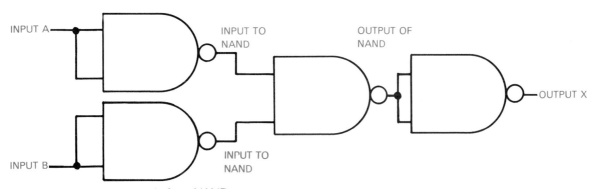

**Figure 5-13.** NOR gate made from NAND gates

| INPUTS | | INPUTS TO NAND | OUTPUT OF NAND | OUTPUT |
|---|---|---|---|---|
| B | A | | | X |
| 0 | 0 | 1 | 1 | 0 | 1 |
| 0 | 1 | 1 | 0 | 1 | 0 |
| 1 | 0 | 0 | 1 | 1 | 0 |
| 1 | 1 | 0 | 0 | 1 | 0 |

**Figure 5-14.** Truth table for a NOR gate made from NAND gates

one type of gate is more economical than buying smaller quantities of two or three different types of gates.

SUMMARY    In this chapter you learned how to make particular gates by using a combination of other gates and also how the NAND gate can be made into any of the other gates. Using these techniques can reduce the cost of a digital device. It is important to learn the method shown in this chapter for finding the possible outputs of a particular circuit (combination of gates) by trying all of the possible input combinations.

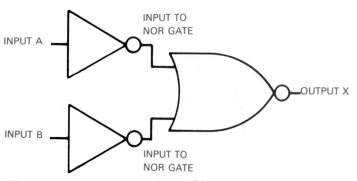

| INPUTS | | INPUTS TO NOR GATE | | OUTPUT |
|---|---|---|---|---|
| B | A | | | X |
| 0 | 0 | | | |
| 0 | 1 | | | |
| 1 | 0 | | | |
| 1 | 1 | | | |

**Figure 5-15.** Inverted inputs to a NOR gate

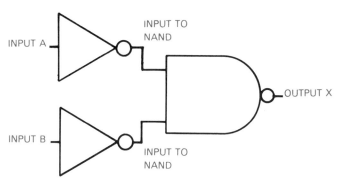

**Figure 5-16.** Inverted inputs to a NAND gate

| INPUTS | | INPUTS TO NOR GATE | | OUTPUT |
|---|---|---|---|---|
| B | A | | | X |
| 0 | 0 | | | |
| 0 | 1 | | | |
| 1 | 0 | | | |
| 1 | 1 | | | |

# REVIEW QUESTIONS

1. Give two advantages of combining extra gates you may already have to make another gate rather than adding another integrated circuit to provide that gate.
2. Draw a diagram of a circuit that uses a combination of two inverters and an OR gate to function as a NAND gate.
3. Draw a diagram of a circuit that uses a combination of two inverters and an AND gate to function as a NOR gate.

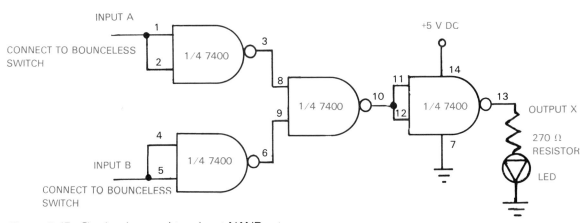

**Figure 5-17.** Circuit using quad two-input NAND gate

4. Fill out the truth table for the circuit diagram shown in Figure 5-15.
5. Fill out the truth table for the circuit diagram shown in Figure 5-16.
6. Make a diagram that shows all of the connections needed to make two NAND gates function as an AND gate.
7. Make a diagram that shows all of the connections needed to make four NAND gates function as a NOR gate.
8. Explain why the NAND gate is sometimes called a universal gate.

## SUGGESTED ACTIVITIES

1. Create a logic circuit using an AND, OR, and NAND gate. The circuit should have only two inputs and one output. Show the truth table for this circuit.
2. Using a quad two-input NAND IC (7400) gate, connect the circuit shown in Figure 5-17, and make a truth table by trying all the possible inputs.

# 6

# USING LOGIC GATES TO DO ARITHMETIC

## OBJECTIVES

After studying this chapter, you will be able to:
- Identify two unusual gates that are made of a combination of gates.
- Understand how logic gates are used to do simple arithmetic problems using the binary system.

## OVERVIEW

Calculators and computers use many of the same types of circuits that you will learn about in this chapter, but on a larger scale in order to handle more complex problems.

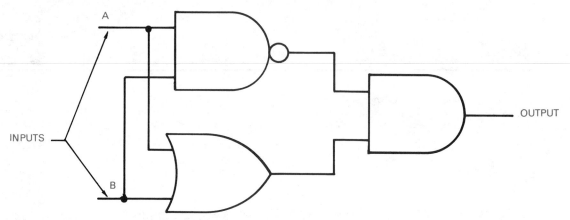

**Figure 6-1.** Exclusive OR gate made from NAND, OR, and AND gates

## EXCLUSIVE OR GATE

The *Exclusive OR* gate is actually a combination of gates that make up a circuit much like those studied in Chapter 5. It is probably the most widely used combination circuit. One of the combinations of gates used to make an Exclusive OR is shown in Figure 6-1. The symbol for an Exclusive OR gate is similar to that of the OR gate except that the curved line across the inputs is added, as in Figure 6-2.

The operation of an Exclusive OR gate is also somewhat similar to an OR gate except that when both inputs A and B are high, the output is 0. Compare the truth tables for an OR gate and an Exclusive OR gate in Figure 6-3.

There are several combinations of gates that will produce the Exclusive OR function. The Exclusive OR function means that only one input or the other, not both, must be a 1 to give a 1 at the output. The Exclusive OR function is similar to the operation of two three-way switches that control a light in the home. If the light is off and you want to turn it on, you can do so with either of the two switches, but not by using both switches. If you flipped both switches at the same instant, the light would

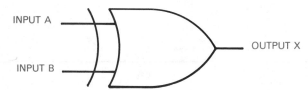

**Figure 6-2.** Symbol for an Exclusive OR gate

| INPUTS | | OUTPUT |
|---|---|---|
| B | A | X |
| 0 | 0 | 0 |
| 0 | 1 | 1 |
| 1 | 0 | 1 |
| 1 | 1 | 1 |

## OR GATE

| INPUTS | | OUTPUT |
|---|---|---|
| B | A | X |
| 0 | 0 | 0 |
| 0 | 1 | 1 |
| 1 | 0 | 1 |
| 1 | 1 | 0 |

## EXCLUSIVE OR GATE

**Figure 6-3.** Truth table for OR gate and for Exclusive OR gate

simply stay off. If you used both switches by flipping first one and then the other, the light would come on but go off when you flipped the second switch. Figure 6–4 diagrams how two three-way switches function much like an Exclusive OR gate.

In Figure 6–4A, the switches are in opposite positions, and the light is off. This state compares to a 0 output. If either switch 1 or switch 2 changed position, as in Figure 6-4B, the light would be on, which would be like a 1 in a digital electronic circuit. In Figure 6–4C, both switches have changed, but the light stays off, which is like a 0 in digital electronics.

The function of an Exclusive OR gate can be compared to the action of two men trying to carry a long sofa through the front door of a house. If neither man goes through the door, then obviously the sofa does not get into the house. This action is similar to the state of an Exclusive OR gate when both inputs are at 0 so that the output is 0. However, if either man carried his end of the sofa in first and the other followed, the sofa would get into the house. This action is like the Exclusive OR gate when either input, but not both inputs, are at 1 so that the output is a 1. If both men try to go through the door at the same time, the sofa does not make it into the house. This situation is similar to the Exclusive OR gate when both inputs are 1s and the output is 0.

The Boolean statement for an Exclusive OR gate is A$\oplus$B = X. The circle around the plus sign means that only one input or the other, not both,

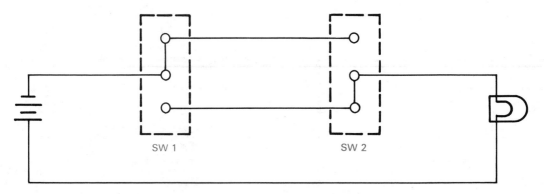

(A) BOTH SWITCHES POSITIONED SO THAT THE LIGHT IS OFF.

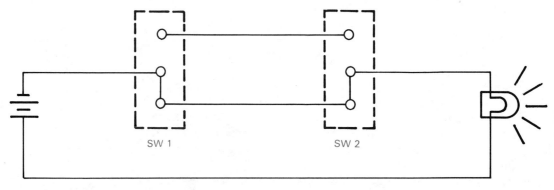

(B) IF EITHER ONE SWITCH OR THE OTHER (IN THIS CASE SWITCH ONE) CHANGED POSITION, THE LIGHT WOULD COME ON.

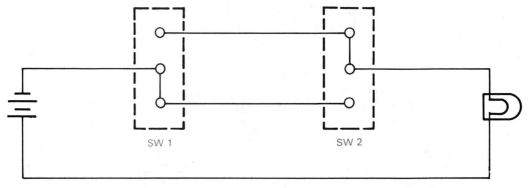

(C) IF BOTH SWITCHES CHANGED FROM THE POSITION IN FIGURE 6-4A, THE LIGHT WOULD STILL BE OFF.

**Figure 6-4.** How three-way switches operate like an Exclusive OR gate

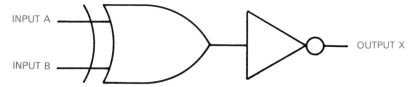

**Figure 6-5.** Exclusive NOR gate made by inverting the output of an Exclusive OR gate

must be a 1 to get a 1 at the output. The statement is read as "A ring sum B equals X."

An *Exclusive NOR* gate is simply an Exclusive OR gate with its output inverted, as shown in Figure 6–5. The symbol for an Exclusive NOR gate appears in Figure 6–6. The truth table for an Exclusive NOR gate is just the opposite of the truth table for an Exclusive OR gate, as shown in Figure 6–7. The Boolean statement for an Exclusive NOR gate is $A \oplus B = X$.

**EXCLUSIVE NOR GATE**

By using digital gates such as those just discussed, a computer can complete large problems in a fraction of a second.

**BINARY ADDITION**

Study the examples of binary addition in Figure 6–8. Problems A, B, and C in Figure 6–8 are simple, and their answers are obvious. Problems D and E are not much more difficult. In problem D, when 1 and 1 are added together in decimal, they equal 2. The binary number 2 is written 10 (one zero). In problem E, $1 + 1 + 1$ in the decimal system would equal 3, but in the binary system it is written as 11 (one one).

In the problems shown in Figure 6–9, when the sums 10 and 11 occur, the digit on the right is recorded, and the 1 is carried on to be added with the next column.

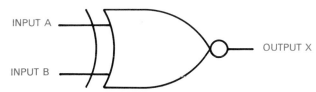

**Figure 6-6.** Symbol for an Exclusive NOR gate

## *Digital Control Valves*

Digital control valves are a cluster of on/off valves arranged in parallel. They control the flow of liquids using a process based on the binary number system. The smallest valve is half the size in area as the next larger size. Each valve in the cluster is twice the size in area as the next smaller one. This arrangement allows the total valve area to be controlled in steps the size of the smallest valve. For example, in an eight-valve cluster, by using all the possible combinations of the valves, 256 steps or increments from closed to open are possible. With ten valves, 1024 different steps could be achieved.

Since the relative sizes of these valves correspond to binary bits 1, 2, 4, 8, etc., the computer program used to control these valves can operate directly in the binary mode which makes the program much faster to execute. The precision and speed of this system gives an advantage over a traditional flow control system.

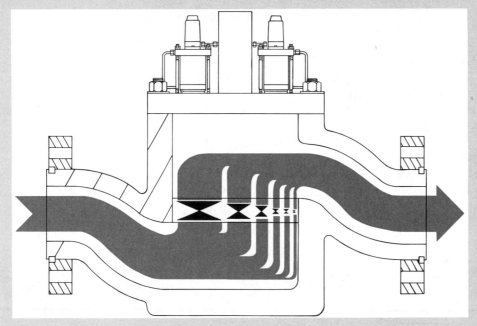

Diagram showing the relative size of valves (courtesy of Digital Valve Company)

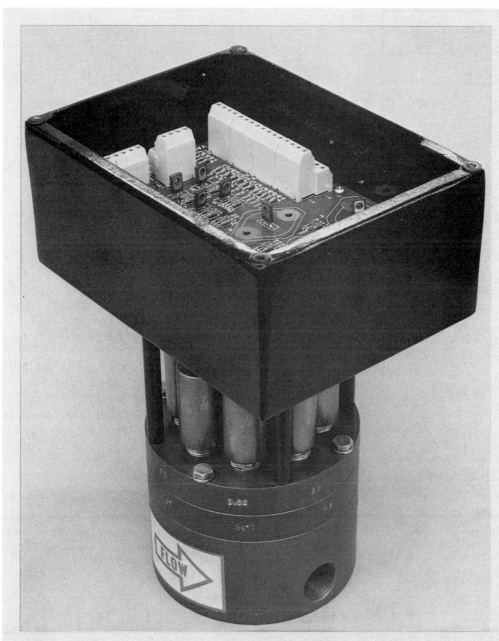

Digital valve and electronic control circuitry (courtesy of Digital Valve Company)

| INPUTS | | OUTPUT |
|---|---|---|
| B | A | X |
| 0 | 0 | 0 |
| 0 | 1 | 1 |
| 1 | 0 | 1 |
| 1 | 1 | 0 |

| INPUTS | | OUTPUT |
|---|---|---|
| B | A | X |
| 0 | 0 | 1 |
| 0 | 1 | 0 |
| 1 | 0 | 0 |
| 1 | 1 | 1 |

# EXCLUSIVE OR GATE

# EXCLUSIVE NOR GATE

**Figure 6-7.** Truth tables for Exclusive OR and Exclusive NOR gates

**HALF ADDER**    By using the combination of logic gates shown in Figure 6-10, you can solve problems A, B, C, and D of Figure 6-8 electronically. The combination of digital logic circuits in the figure is called a *half adder*. Because it has only two inputs, it is limited in the addition problems it can perform; it cannot add $1 + 1 + 1$.

Follow through the logic gates to see how the circuit operates in working the problem in Figure 6-11. An AND gate and an XOR (Exclusive OR) gate can be used to make a circuit that will add any two bits. In Figure

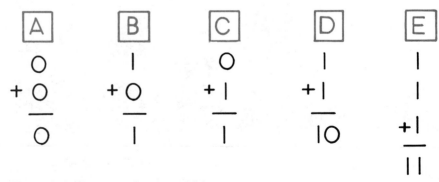

**Figure 6-8.** Examples of binary addition

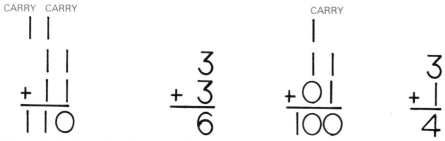

**Figure 6-9.** Examples of binary addition showing the carrying process

6-11, input A of the AND gate and input A of the XOR gate are connected together to form one input. The other input is made by connecting input B of both gates together. This connection will cause both gates to have similar inputs. The trick to getting the proper addition results is to make the output of the AND gate be the carry column and the output of the XOR gate be the sum column. LEDs can be used to show the outputs.

To add $0 + 0$, which equals 0, both inputs of the circuit should be at 0. Both the AND gate and the XOR gate have 0 outputs if their inputs are 0. Therefore, both the carry and the sum are 0, Figure 6-11A.

If 1 and 0 are added together, the outcome is 1. In this case, one input of each gate should be a 1, and the other input of each gate should be a 0. The 1

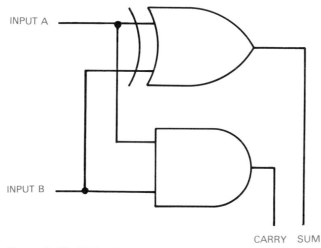

**Figure 6-10.** Half adder made from two logic gates

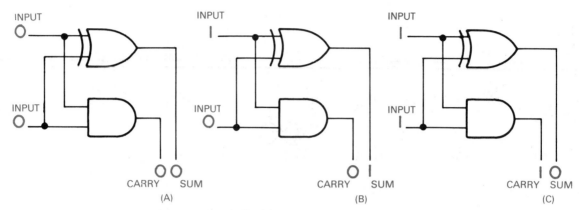

**Figure 6-11.** Doing binary addition with a half adder

and 0 at inputs of the XOR will cause its output to be a 1. Thus, the sum is 1. However, the 1 and 0 at the inputs of the AND gate cause its output, which is the carry, to be 0. The correct answer of 0 1 is shown at the output, as in Figure 6-11B. Zero and 1 added together will give the same results as 1 and 0 added. Therefore, the digital circuit will work in exactly the same way.

When 1 and 1 are added, the result is 10 (or 2 in the decimal system). Both gates should have a 1 at each of their inputs. The XOR gate will have a 0 output with 1 and 1 at its inputs; therefore, the sum is 0. However, the AND gate will finally have a 1 at its output because of the 1s at both of its inputs. The carry will be a 1 also. The correct answer of 10 (one, zero) is shown at the outputs in Figure 6-11C.

This circuit did not perform any magic, but it certainly caused the correct outputs to show the answer to each combination of inputs being added together.

## FULL ADDER

With the half adder, it is not possible to solve addition problems requiring three inputs. However, by using two half-adder circuits and an OR gate connected as in Figure 6-12, it is possible to add 1 + 1 + 1 because this circuit has three inputs. To add 1 + 1 + 1, inputs A, B, and C would be 1s as shown in Figure 6-12. Inputs B and C would make the inputs of the XOR of the first half adder both be 1s, and the output of XOR would be a 0. The output at this XOR is connected to one of the inputs of the XOR of the second half adder and to one of the inputs to an AND gate. The other input of the XOR in the second half adder is input A. The 0 from the first half adder

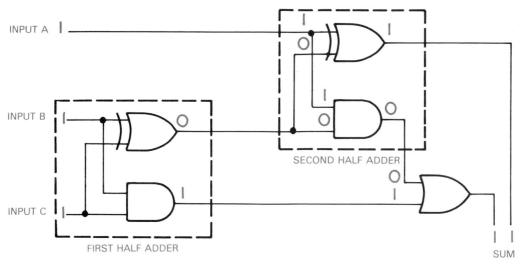

**Figure 6-12.** *Full adder made from two half-adders and an OR gate. Inputs 1, 1, and 1 are added to result in an output of 11.*

and the 1 from input A cause the XOR in the second half adder to give a 1 at the output labeled "sum."

Inputs B and C put 1s to both inputs of the AND of the first half adder, making the output of this AND a 1. The output of 1 from the AND is connected to the OR gate, making the output of the OR gate a 1 no matter what its other input is. The output of the OR gate is labeled "carry." The answer is shown as 1 1 (or 3 in decimal), which is correct.

The *full-adder* circuit can correctly add any combination of 1s and 0s at its three inputs. Two examples are shown in Figure 6-13. A full adder is shown in the block diagram of Figure 6-14.

Figure 6-15 shows a full adder with its inputs and outputs arranged so they can connect together several full adders. Full adders may also be connected together in an IC. The 7483 IC is called a four-bit full adder because it can take any two four-bit (four-digit) numbers and add them together. The 7483 is made up of four full adders. The "carry" output of each of the first three full adders is connected inside the IC to one of the three inputs (carry in) of the next full adder. Figure 6-16 is a block diagram of the 7483. With additional circuitry the 7483 can also be used to do binary subtraction.

In order to connect 7483 ICs together, each is provided with connections that allow the "carry" to pass from one to the other just as it passes from one full adder to another inside the IC. To identify these

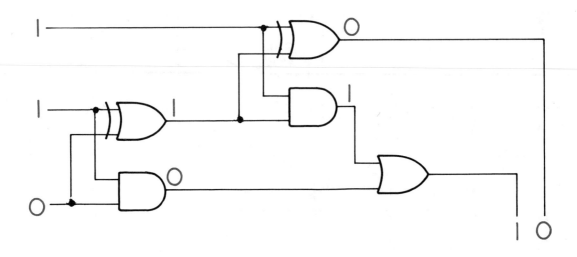

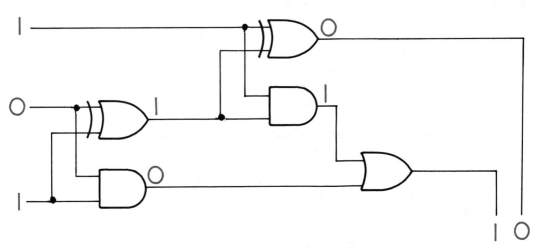

**Figure 6-13.** Two examples of a full adder solving an addition problem

**Figure 6-14.** Block diagram of a full adder

connections the input connection of the first full adder (FA1) is called the "carry in," and the carry of the fourth full adder (FA4) is called the "carry out." This carry out indicates the digit that is furthest to the left.

Figure 6-17 diagrams a 7483 IC used to add the numbers 1000 to 1001. To prove mathematically that the circuit is added correctly, follow through the problem in Figure 6-18.

The first column of numbers on the right is added by FA1 (full adder 1). The top number is the input at A, and the bottom number is the input at B. The second column of numbers is added by FA2, etc. As explained before, if there is a carry at any of the full adders except FA4, it is passed on to the next

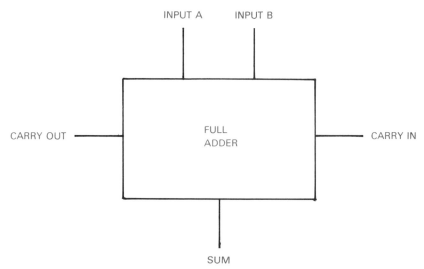

**Figure 6-15.** Full adder arranged for connection to other full adders

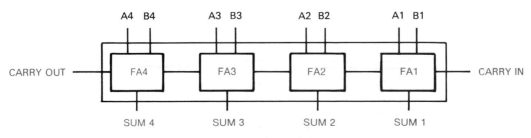

**Figure 6-16.** Block diagram of the 7483 IC containing four full adders

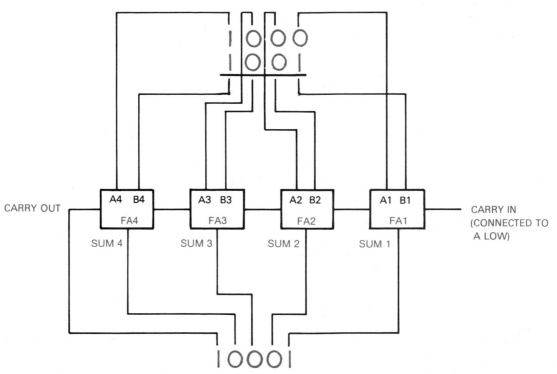

**Figure 6-17.** Diagram of full adder being used for addition

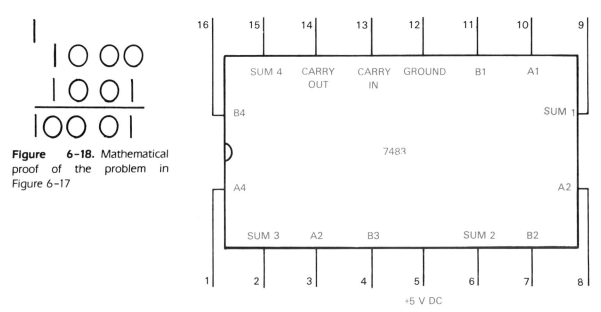

Figure 6-18. Mathematical proof of the problem in Figure 6-17

Figure 6-19. Pin-out diagram for a 7483 IC containing four full adders

full adder. The outputs of the full adders along with the carry out of FA4 make up the total sum or answer to the problem. The pin-out diagram for a 7483 appears in Figure 6–19. This IC is useful not only because it can add four-bit numbers, but also because with some added circuitry, it can subtract.

## BINARY SUBTRACTION

Although binary subtraction can be done in a method similar to subtracting in the decimal system, a different method has been devised to subtract electronically by making a few changes in the circuitry used for addition. A popular way to subtract in binary is to invert the smaller number that is being subtracted (inverting in binary simply means to change a 0 to a 1 or a 1 to a 0). Add 1 to the smaller number; add the two numbers together, and drop the last carry. Study the example for subtracting in binary in Figure 6–20.

Although this method is a little more difficult to do on paper than some other methods of subtraction, it allows the use of the 7483 chip four-bit full adder. In order to do subtraction the 7483 requires the added circuitry shown in Figure 6–21.

The inverters connected in series with the B inputs invert the small or bottom number of the subtraction problem. By connecting the carry in of

**Figure 6-20.** Subtracting in binary

the first full adder to a high, or 1, a 1 is added to the inverted bottom number. Finally, by not using the carry-out connection of the 7483, there is no carry out or fifth bit to deal with.

Although the circuit in Figure 6-21 works quite well, it does require rewiring each time you wish to change from addition to subtraction. Figure 6-22 shows a circuit that operates much like a calculator because by changing a switch from one position to another, you change the circuit from an adder to a subtractor.

Before examining how the circuit in Figure 6-22 operates, review the operation of an Exclusive OR gate and see how it functions as a controlled inverter in the circuit of Figure 6-23. In this circuit when the input B is connected to a 1, the Exclusive OR inverts the input of the A to give an output at X that is opposite the A. The truth table for an Exclusive OR gate appears in Figure 6-24.

In Figure 6-23 input B or the XOR is connected through a switch to a high, or 1. The input at A equals 0. Therefore, the output at X is 1. When

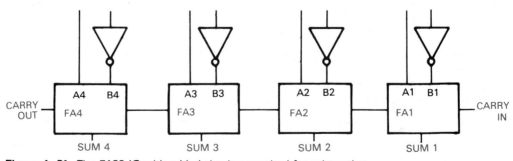

**Figure 6-21.** The 7483 IC with added circuitry required for subtraction

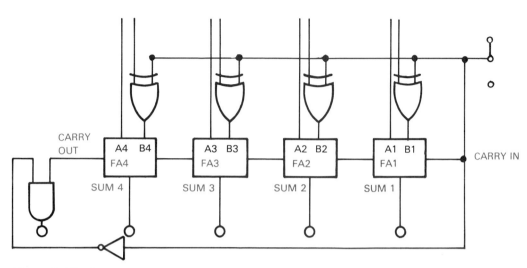

**Figure 6-22.** Circuit that may be used for addition or subtraction

input A is changed to a 1, both inputs A and B are 1's, as shown in Figure 6-25, and the output is 0.

If it is not necessary to use the XOR for inverting (for doing addition), then the input B should be connected to a 0, and whatever is put to input A comes out unchanged at output X. In Figure 6-26, if input A is a 1 and B is 0, then output X of the XOR will be a 1. On the other hand, if input A is 0 and B is 0, the output X of the XOR will be 0.

In the process of doing binary subtraction shown earlier in this chapter, it was necessary not only to invert the bottom row of numbers but

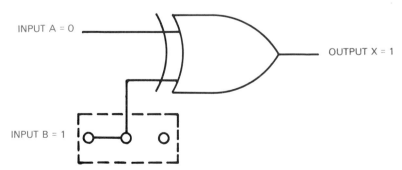

**Figure 6-23.** Exclusive OR circuit functioning as a controlled inverter. Input A is inverted at output X.

| INPUTS | | OUTPUT |
|---|---|---|
| B | A | X |
| 0 | 0 | 0 |
| 0 | 1 | 1 |
| 1 | 0 | 1 |
| 1 | 1 | 0 |

**Figure 6-24.** Truth table for an Exclusive OR gate

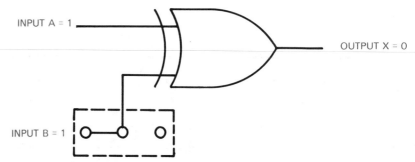

**Figure 6-25.** Controlled inverter with A at 1

also to add 1 to that inverted number. To add 1 electronically, connect the carry in of the first full adder to a 1. If the carry in is connected to the same switch as that used to control the XORs when the XORs are in the subtraction mode (inverting the inputs), the carry in adds a 1 to the inverted number. On the other hand, when the switch controlling the XORs is at a low (0), then not only do the XORs not invert the input, but also there is a 0 at the carry in.

The switch that allows the circuit to be changed from a full adder to a full subtractor is called the controller and is like the function switch on a calculator that allows you to do either addition or subtraction. Figure 6-27 shows how the controller switch connects to both the XORs and the carry in. To make this circuit do both addition and subtraction, it is necessary to shut off or blank out the carry out when subtracting, Figure 6-28.

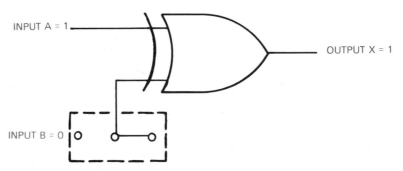

**Figure 6-26.** Exclusive OR gate with input B connected to a low. This circuit does not function as an inverter.

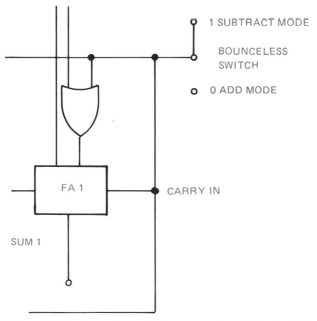

**Figure 6-27.** Controller switch connected to Exclusive ORs and carry in

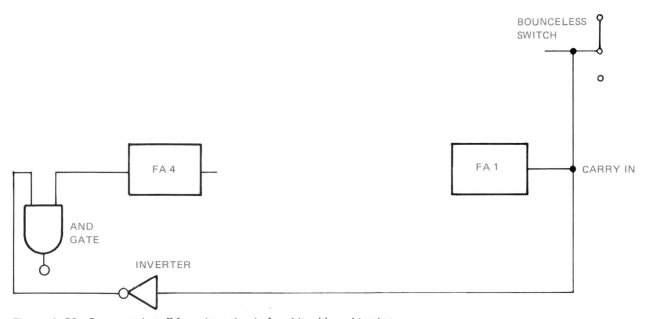

**Figure 6-28.** Carry-out shutoff for subtraction in four-bit adder-subtractor

95

When the controller switch is at 1, the inverter puts a 0 to the input of the AND gate. A 0 at the AND gate input keeps the output of the AND gate at 0, even though the other input may be at a 1, because of a 1 at the carry out of the last full adder. This placement of components keeps the output display connected to the carry out from indicating a 1 when subtracting.

If the controller switch is at 0 for addition, then the inverter puts a 1 at the AND gate, and if there is a 1 at the carry out, there is a 1 at the output of the AND gate. The circuit in Figure 6–28 is called a four-bit adder-subtractor and is a simple calculator.

## SUMMARY

In this chapter you learned that an Exclusive OR gate is made up of a combination of gates and differs from a regular OR gate in that when both inputs to a two-input XOR are a 1, the output is 0.

You also learned to add in binary and to add together numbers by using a combination of logic gates. By making the outputs represent the sum and carry of an addition problem, you can get the correct answer to the problem from the logic gates.

Subtracting in binary is a little more difficult than binary addition because you must take several steps to get the answer. XOR gates are used as controlled inverters. You add 1 to the carry in, and gates keep the output of the carry out from being shown. Thus, the full-adder circuit can also be used for binary subtraction.

## REVIEW QUESTIONS

1. Complete the truth table in Figure 6–29 for an Exclusive OR gate.
2. Add the following problems in binary: $10 + 11$, $111 + 101$, $1001 + 0110$.

| INPUTS | | OUTPUT |
|---|---|---|
| B | A | X |
| 0 | 0 | |
| 0 | 1 | |
| 1 | 0 | |
| 1 | 1 | |

**Figure 6–29.** Truth table for an Exclusive OR gate

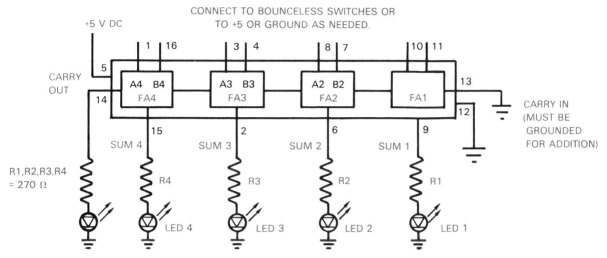

**Figure 6-30.** Circuit using a 7483 full adder

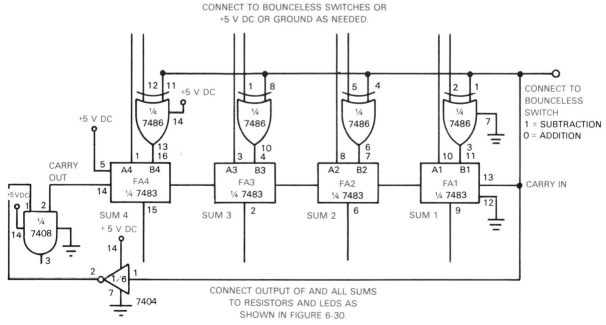

**Figure 6-31.** Circuit that may be used for addition or subtraction

3. What is a disadvantage of a half adder as compared to a full adder?
4. When doing addition, the carry in of a full adder must be connected to a _____.
5. Subtract the following numbers in binary using the process shown in this chapter, and show your work: $101 - 010$, $1100 - 0100$.
6. Diagram an XOR, and explain how it can be used as an inverter.
7. What must the input at the carry in of a 7483 four-bit full adder be when it is used for subtraction?
8. Draw a diagram and explain how the output indicator of the carry out of a full adder can be kept at 0 when subtracting.

## SUGGESTED ACTIVITIES

1. Secure a 7483 integrated circuit and connect the circuit shown in Figure 6–30. Do several addition problems with this circuit.
2. Using a 7483 and a 7486 quad two-input XOR, a 7408 quad two-input AND gate, and a 7404 hex inverter, connect the circuit in Figure 6–31, and do several subtraction problems with it.

# FLIP-FLOP CIRCUITS

## OBJECTIVES

After studying this chapter, you will be able to:
- Explain how digital electronics can be used to store data.
- Build circuits used for data storage from familiar logic gates.

## OVERVIEW

One of the many advantages that calculators and computers have over adding machines is the ability to store numbers until they are needed. Computers must also be able to store large amounts of data in order to have it available when needed for processing. The circuits you will learn about in this chapter are used to store information only temporarily. Although information can be put in and taken out of these circuits easily, it is lost as soon as the electrical power is shut off.

The logic gates and circuits you studied in earlier chapters made decisions based upon the inputs present at that moment. Memory circuits, however, can recall a history of inputs and make decisions based upon them and current inputs. Just as previous circuits made decisions that resulted in a conclusion of either a 1 or a 0, memory circuits also remember only a 1 or a 0.

## MEMORY CAPABILITY

In a simple memory circuit, such as that shown in Figure 7-1, if the input at A is 1, then the output becomes a 1. The output will now stay at a 1 no matter what happens to input A. The reason the output stays at a 1 is that whenever you have a 1 at either input or both of the inputs to an OR gate, the output is a 1. In this case the output of the OR gate gives an input of 1 to B. Although this circuit does remember a 1, it is awkward to reset when you need to change the data you want stored.

## RS FLIP-FLOP

The *RS flip-flop* circuit is a memory circuit that you can set to a particular output, then reset easily when you need to change data. The RS in the term "RS flip-flop" circuit stands for "reset and set." The term "flip-flop" comes from the fact that this circuit, unlike any other that has been discussed up to this point, has two outputs. These outputs are always opposite. If one is a 0, the other is a 1; if one changes, the other will change to the opposite state (1 or 0) at the same time.

The RS flip-flop in Figure 7-2 uses two NOR gates. The output of each NOR gate connects to one of the inputs of the other. The data is entered at the two remaining inputs, which are called set and reset. Since the outputs are always at opposite states, if one is called Q, the other is called "not Q" ($\overline{Q}$). (The bar over the letter stands for "not.")

Follow through the circuit in Figure 7-2 by putting a 1 to input S and a 0 to input R. It may be helpful to refer to the truth table for a NOR gate, shown in Figure 7-3, to see that any time that there is a 1 at an input of a NOR gate, the output is a 0. Therefore, the 1 at the set input causes output $\overline{Q}$ (not Q) to be a 0.

The output $\overline{Q}$ of NOR gate #1 is connected to one of the inputs of NOR gate #2, making that input a 0. If the other input (reset) is also a 0, the output Q of NOR gate #2 will be a 1. If the set input of NOR gate #1 is changed to a 0, the output at Q will be 0 because the other input to NOR gate #1 continues to be a 1. Except for the first time data is received at the set input, the data can be changed repeatedly, and the outputs will stay the same.

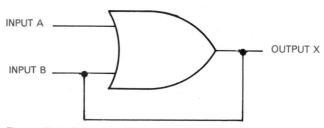

**Figure 7-1.** OR gate with memory capability

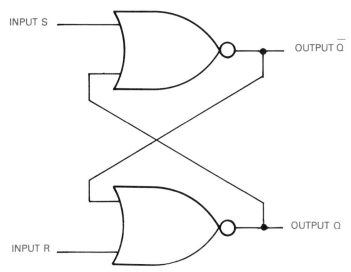

**Figure 7-2.** RS flip-flop made from two NOR gates

To change or reset this flip-flop circuit, put a 0 at the set input and a 1 at the reset input. The 1 applied to the NOR gate #2 makes the output Q go to 0, Figure 7-4. Now the NOR gate #1 receives the 0 input from output Q, and the 0 from its set input. Therefore, the output $\overline{Q}$ of the NOR gate #1 becomes a 1. The truth table for this circuit appears in Figure 7-5. As you can see from the truth table, you should avoid setting both inputs R and S to 1. If they are both set to 1, both Q and $\overline{Q}$ will try to go to the same state. Eventually one NOR gate stays at a 1 and the other goes to 0. However, they

| INPUTS | | OUTPUT |
|---|---|---|
| B | A | X |
| 0 | 0 | 1 |
| 0 | 1 | 0 |
| 1 | 0 | 0 |
| 1 | 1 | 0 |

**Figure 7-3.** Truth table for a NOR gate

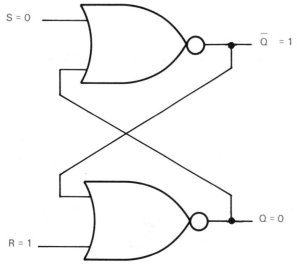

| INPUTS | | OUTPUTS | |
|---|---|---|---|
| R | S | Q | $\overline{Q}$ |
| 0 | 0 | NO CHANGE | |
| 0 | 1 | 1 | 0 |
| 1 | 0 | 0 | 1 |
| 1 | 1 | RACE CONDITION | |

**Figure 7-5.** Truth table for an RS flip-flop

**Figure 7-4.** RS flip-flop showing Q reset to 0

arrived at these states accidentally and may not do the same thing each time. This state of having both R and S set to 1 is called the *race condition*.

Rather than draw the schematic diagram for each flip-flop circuit, symbols are used to identify them. The symbol for the RS flip-flop is shown in Figure 7-6.

RS flip-flops can also be made with NAND gates. With a NAND gate, when S = 0 and R = 1, Q would be 1. When S = 1 and R = 0, Q would be 0, Figure 7-7.

**CLOCK INPUT**    A feature that can be added to the RS flip-flop is a third input, called a *clock input,* that controls when the inputs can change the output. This feature is necessary in calculators and computers to make sure that all of the data is entered before the flip-flops act on it. For example, if you were adding the numbers 3462 and 1875 together, you would not want the calculator to add the 2 of 3462 to the 5 of 1875 until you had the entire number entered and were sure that it was correct.

In Figure 7-8 you can see how the addition of two logic gates to an RS flip-flop can control the circuit. If the clock input is held at a 0, the output of the two AND gates will be 0 no matter what the inputs at R and S are. When the clock input is changed to a 1, then if either the S or R input is a 1, a 1 is passed on to the NOR gates of the RS flip-flop.

The action of the clock input can be compared to a time lock on a bank vault. Only during a certain time period can the bank vault be unlocked.

## The Mark I Computer

A milestone in the history of computers was the completion of the Mark I in 1944. A Harvard University professor named Howard Aiken had been working on it, along with engineers and technicians from the IBM Corporation, since 1937. The Mark I weighed in at almost 5 tons, and was 55 feet long. Inside it, thousands of electromechanical relays and mechanical counters performed various mathematical calculations. Overall the Mark I was noisy and slow compared to the computers of the 1980s.

In the years following World War II, completely electronic computers were built using vacuum tubes. By 1960 solid-state computers were being built, which were smaller and required less electricity to operate. The development of digital circuits and microprocessors has made it possible to create compact computers with more speed, memory, and efficiency than the giant Mark I. Today the Mark I is on display at Harvard for interested visitors to see.

The MARK I computer (courtesy of IBM Corporation)

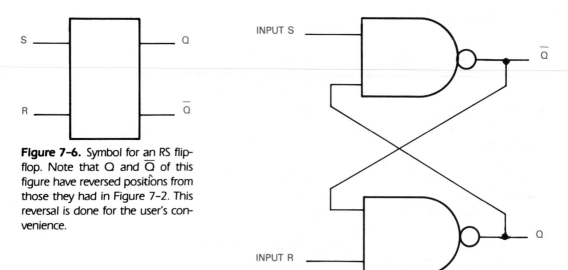

**Figure 7-6.** Symbol for an RS flip-flop. Note that Q and $\overline{Q}$ of this figure have reversed positions from those they had in Figure 7-2. This reversal is done for the user's convenience.

**Figure 7-7.** RS flip-flop made with NAND gates

Only when the clock input is high can the RS flip-flop act on the data at its inputs.

## D FLIP-FLOP

Earlier in this chapter you learned that there are some input combinations you should avoid when using an RS flip-flop. One way to be sure that the set and reset inputs are always opposite is to add a *D flip-flop* circuit, as shown in Figure 7-9.

The S (set) and R (reset) inputs in this flip-flop allow you to control the output states in spite of the data at input D. Since the D flip-flop has only one data input (D), whatever is at that input will be passed on to the Q input if the clock is high. To allow the input (1 or 0) to be selected, the clock input is held low. Only when the clock input goes high will the data be passed on to the outputs.

Because the data at input D must wait until the clock input goes high, this flip-flop is called a DELAY or D flip-flop. Also since the data passes from input to output just as the clock goes high, the flip-flop is said to be triggered on the *leading edge* of the clock pulse, Figure 7-10. (A *clock pulse* is a volt-

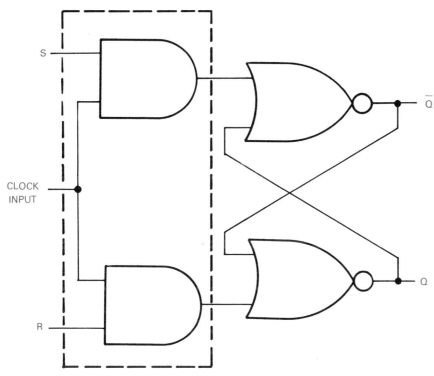

**Figure 7-8.** Clock input added to an RS flip-flop. The area in the dotted lines is the added clock input circuitry.

age change at regular intervals. How clock pulses are generated will be discussed later.) Figure 7–11 shows the symbol for a D flip-flop.

Keep in mind that once the data in memory circuits is passed to the outputs, any number of changes in the set input will not affect the output.

## JK FLIP-FLOP

The *JK flip-flop* is the most complex of the flip-flop circuits. It has some advantages over the other flip-flops because of its additional circuitry. It is the most popular flip-flop because of the many ways it can be used in digital logic circuits.

Although there are several kinds of JK flip-flops, a very common type is that made up of two interconnected RS flip-flops. One of the RS flip-flops acts as the *master,* and the other acts as a *slave*. This type of flip-flop is referred to as a JK (*master-slave*) flip-flop. Figure 7–12 shows the general makeup of a JK (master-slave) flip-flop.

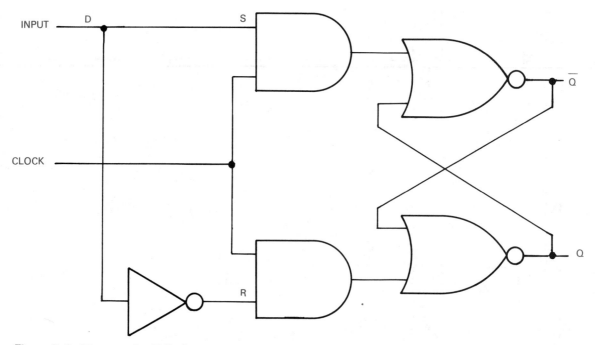

**Figure 7-9.** Diagram of a D flip-flop

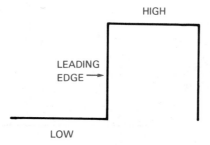

**Figure 7-10.** Diagram of the leading edge of a clock pulse

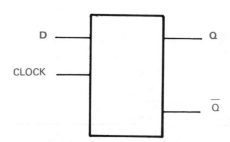

**Figure 7-11.** Symbol for a D flip-flop

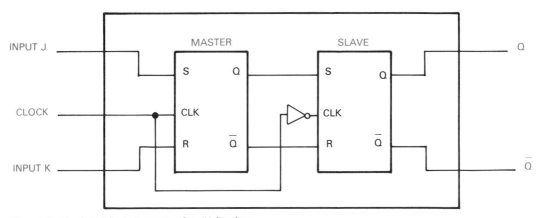

**Figure 7-12.** Simplified diagram of a JK flip-flop

The master RS flip-flop is set or reset (depending upon the inputs) when the clock pulse goes high or is held high. The slave flip-flop does not change at this time because the clock pulse to it is inverted (goes low). Since the outputs of the master flip-flop control the slave flip-flop, when the clock pulse goes low, the inverted clock pulse at the slave flip-flop causes the slave flip-flop to copy the action of the master flip-flop.

Only when the clock pulse goes from high voltage to a low voltage (*trailing edge*) do the outputs of the JK flip-flop change or react to the inputs, Figure 7-13. If both the J and K inputs are 0, the flip-flop is disabled, and the outputs do not change states. If J is a 1 and K is a 0, then the outputs will go to $Q = 1$ and $\overline{Q} = 0$. If they are already in that state ($Q = 1$ and $\overline{Q} = 0$), they will just stay there. However, if $J = 0$ and $K = 1$, then Q will go to a 0 and $\overline{Q}$ to a 1 unless, of course, they are already in that state.

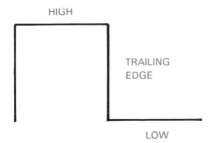

**Figure 7-13.** Diagram of the trailing edge of the clock pulse

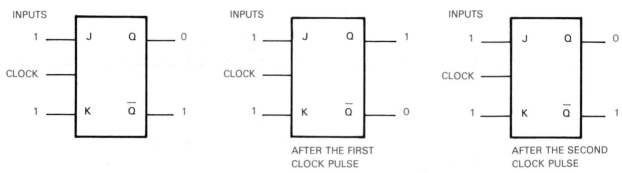

**Figure 7-14.** Diagram showing operation of a JK flip-flop when both J and K are 1's.

Finally, one of the most important actions that happens with a JK flip-flop is when J is at 1 and K is at 1. Even though this state could cause a race condition with other flip-flops, it is not a problem with the JK flip-flop. When both J and K are at 1, whatever state Q and Q are in (1 or 0), they will change to the opposite state on the trailing edge of the clock pulse. For example, if Q is at 0 and $\overline{Q}$ is at 1, on the trailing edge of the clock pulse, Q will change to a 1 and $\overline{Q}$ to a 0. Figure 7-14 shows the operation of the JK flip-flop when both J and K are 1.

This operation of changing states is sometimes called "toggling" and is used to make JK flip-flops into counters and other useful digital circuits. Study the truth table for a JK flip-flop in Figure 7-15.

The S (set) and R (reset) inputs to the JK flip-flop allow the outputs to be changed (set or reset) without a clock pulse. They are used to either put data into or clear data from a flip-flop. Since S (set) is used to put data into a JK flip-flop before any clock pulses occur, it is called the preset (PR) by many manufacturers of ICs. Similarly, since reset (R) is used to clear out data from flip-flops, it is called clear (CLR). The CLR (clear) input of a JK flip-flop is used to clear the memory of a calculator.

For many applications of the JK flip-flop, the PR and CLR inputs are left floating (disconnected). In order for the output not to be affected by this floating (high input) condition, called floating high, the circuit is designed so that either the PR or CLR input (never both at the same time) must be momentarily connected to a 0 to change the outputs of the flip-flop.

Figure 7-16 shows the symbol of a JK flip-flop. The bubble on the PR and CLR inputs indicates that the input must be low to cause a change in the outputs. Figure 7-17 shows the pin-out of a 7476 IC that includes two JK flip-flops.

| INPUTS | | OUTPUTS | |
|:---:|:---:|:---:|:---:|
| K | J | Q | $\overline{Q}$ |
| 0 | 0 | NO CHANGE | |
| 0 | 1 | *1 | ·0 |
| 1 | 0 | *0 | *1 |
| 1 | 1 | *OUTPUTS CHANGE | |

**Figure 7-15.** Truth table for a JK flip-flop

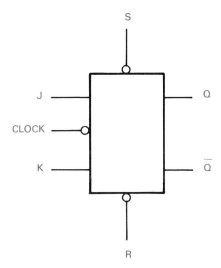

**Figure 7-16.** Symbol for a JK flip-flop

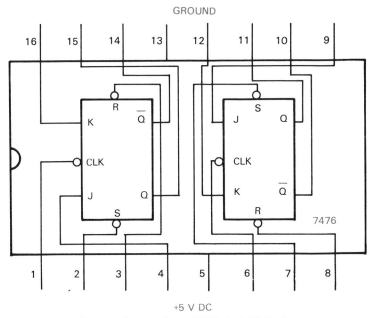

**Figure 7-17.** Pin-out diagram for a 7476 dual JK flip-flop

**CLOCK PULSES**         Since JK and other flip-flops operate on clock pulses, it is important to understand how clock pulses are generated. One way to generate clock pulses would be to flip a switch on and off numerous times. However, this could not give a fast rate of pulses and before long either the operator would tire or the switch would wear out. A better way to generate clock pulses is to do it electronically with a 555 timer circuit, a Schmidt trigger, or with other circuits, Figure 7-18. These circuits create pulses by rapidly turning transistors on and off. Some of these timer circuits can be adjusted from producing a few pulses per second all the way to producing millions of pulses per second.

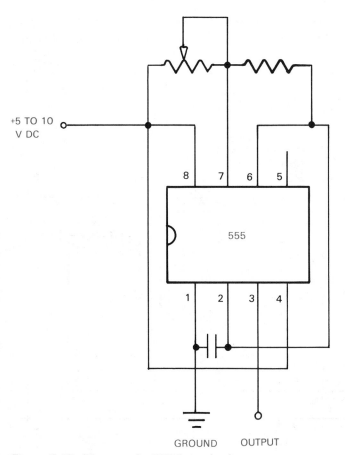

**Figure 7-18.** Diagram of a 555 timer circuit

In this chapter you learned that some types of digital circuits can remember the data that is put into them even though the inputs change. These circuits normally have two outputs. The outputs are always in opposite states. Thus, when they change states, they simply trade with each other. Because of this action of trading states with each other, these circuits are called flip-flops.

One of the simplest flip-flop circuits is the RS flip-flop. It has two inputs—a set and a reset. Once data has been entered at the set input, further data at the set input has no effect on the output. Only after the circuit has been reset can further data affect the output.

In the D-type flip-flops, the inputs are set up so that they are always in opposite states. This precaution prevents the race condition possible with the RS flip-flop.

**SUMMARY**

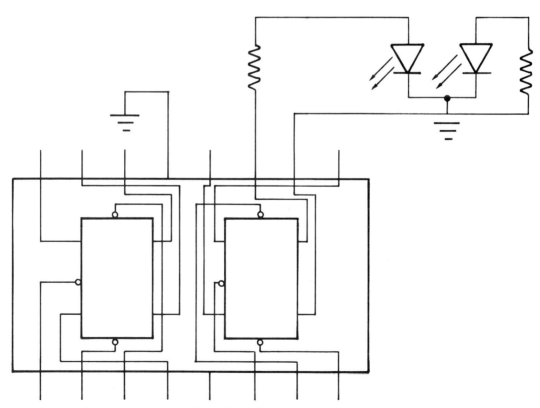

**Figure 7-19.** Circuit to be wired with a JK flip-flop

Finally, you learned that the JK flip-flop is controlled by a clock pulse and is triggered by the trailing edge of a clock pulse. It is not possible to put the JK flip-flop in the race condition. In fact, when both inputs are at a 1, the outputs simply change states at the trailing edge of the next clock pulse. The JK flip-flop is used extensively for counter and memory circuits.

## REVIEW QUESTIONS

1. Explain how a memory circuit operation is different from the operation of an ordinary logic gate.

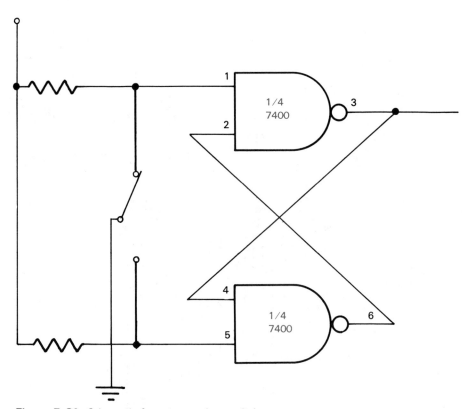

**Figure 7-20.** Schematic for a bounceless switch

2. If the Q output of an RS flip-flop is a 1 when S = 0 and R = 1, what will S and R need to be to change Q to a 1?

3. In a JK flip-flop, if J = 1 and K = 0, what will the outputs Q and $\overline{Q}$ be after the next clock pulse?

4. In a JK flip-flop, if J = 0 and K = 1, what will the outputs Q and $\overline{Q}$ be after the next clock pulse?

5. If both inputs J and K are at a 1 and the outputs are Q = 1 and $\overline{Q}$ = 0, what will the output be after the next clock pulse?

6. Is the JK flip-flop triggered on the leading edge or the trailing edge of the clock pulse?

7. How can the outputs of a JK flip-flop be changed without waiting for a clock pulse?

8. To change the Q output of a JK flip-flop to a 0, what does the R (reset) input have to be?

## SUGGESTED ACTIVITIES

1. Bounceless switches are used to make sure that a digital circuit receives only one pulse when a switch is opened or closed. Using a 7476 dual JK flip-flop, wire the circuit shown in Figure 7–19. Be sure to use a "bounceless" switch for the clock input pin 6. The schematic for a bounceless switch is shown in Figure 7–20.

2. Make input J of flip-flop 1 a 1 by connecting pin 9 to the +5 V DC.

3. Make input K of flip-flop 1 low by connecting pin 12 to ground.

4. Toggle switch 1 (turn it on and then off). This will give the flip-flop one clock pulse.

5. If the LED connected to Q is not already on, it should come on after you toggle switch 1. This indicates that Q of flip-flop 1 is at a 1. Next change input K to a high by connecting pin 12 to +5 V DC.

6. Toggle the switch once more. The LED connected to Q of flip-flop 1 should go out and the LED connected to $\overline{Q}$ of flip-flop 1 should go on. Put away all equipment and components used in this experiment.

# 8

# SHIFT REGISTERS

## OBJECTIVES

After studying this chapter, you will be able to:
- Identify from a schematic diagram a serial shift-register circuit and a parallel shift-register circuit.
- List uses for each type of shift register and give advantages and disadvantages of each.
- Predict the correct outputs of a shift register when given specific inputs.

## OVERVIEW

Shift registers are used extensively in computers. They provide a place to store data until it is to be processed. Data may also be changed while it is in the shift register by adding to it or subtracting from it. The shift registers discussed in this chapter are made up of combinations of JK flip-flops that were discussed in Chapter 7.

Serial-load shift registers are made by simply connecting a number of JK flip-flops in line with each other. The data is input into the first flip-flop (FF1), then transferred from flip-flop to flip-flop whenever a clock pulse occurs. Study Figure 8-1 to understand how the data is moved through the shift register.

To make certain that there is no unwanted data in this shift register, it is a good idea to clear it just as you would a calculator. Momentarily touching the lead connected to all of the resets to a low makes all of the Qs 0s if they are not already in that state.

To input data, put a 1 to input A. Input K will be a 0 because of the inverter connected to it. J will be a 1 and K a 0, which will make the output Q of FFA a 1 after the next clock pulse. The other FFs will remain unchanged because prior to the clock pulse, all of the input Js were at 0. They were being held there because they are connected to the Qs, which were reset to 0.

After the first clock pulse, the outputs would appear as in Figure 8-2. As you can see from the indicator light of FF1, a 1 has been entered into the shift register and is being stored there. It will then become an input for FF2. At this point, J of FF1 is manually set back to 0.

The second clock pulse will cause the output Q of FF2 to change to a 1 because input J is a 1 and input K is a 0. The Q output of FF1 will go to 0 because input J is 0 and K is a 1. Now the outputs of the shift register appear as in Figure 8-3.

## SERIAL-LOAD SHIFT REGISTERS

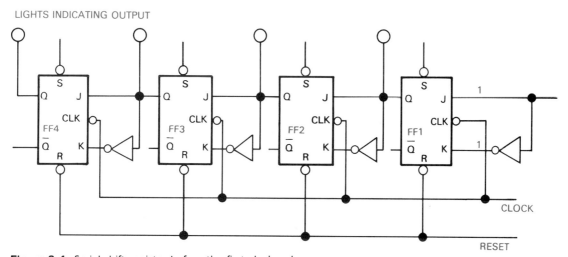

LIGHTS INDICATING OUTPUT

**Figure 8-1.** Serial shift register before the first clock pulse

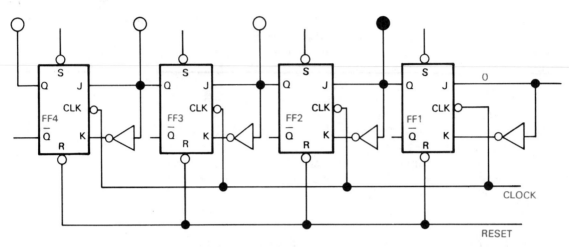

**Figure 8-2.** Serial shift register after the first clock pulse

Before the third clock pulse occurs, only the J input of FF3 is a 1 and K is 0. The other J inputs are 0, and the other K inputs are 1s. The third clock pulse causes the output Q of FF3 to go to a 1, Figure 8-4.

One more clock pulse will shift the 1 to FF4. The outputs will appear as in Figure 8-5. Finally, on the fifth clock pulse, the 1 would be shifted out of the shift register, and all of the outputs would be back at 0. The process of shifting the data (in this case a 1) from flip-flop to flip-flop is what gives the circuit its name of "shift register."

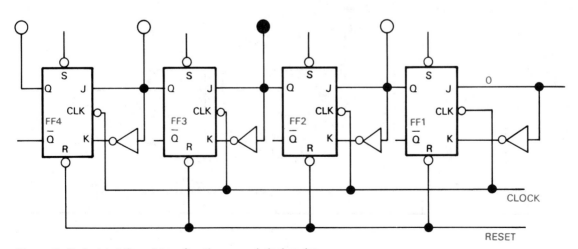

**Figure 8-3.** Serial shift register after the second clock pulse

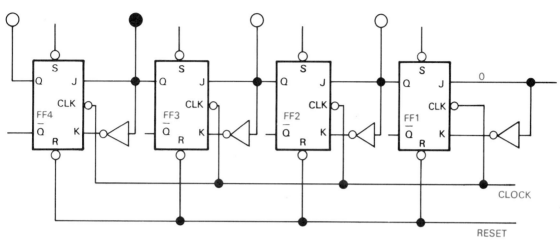

**Figure 8-4.** Serial shift register after the third clock pulse

Since all of the data must be entered through the J input of FF1 and shifted over to the other flip-flop, this type of shift register is called a serial-load shift register. Figure 8-6 shows the data moving from right to left because of the clock pulse. To enter a binary number such as 1001, the J input of FF1 would have to be set to the positions shown in Figure 8-7 for each clock pulse. The serial-load shift register can be easily reconnected to shift data in the opposite direction (left to right). Figure 8-8 illustrates the reconnected circuit.

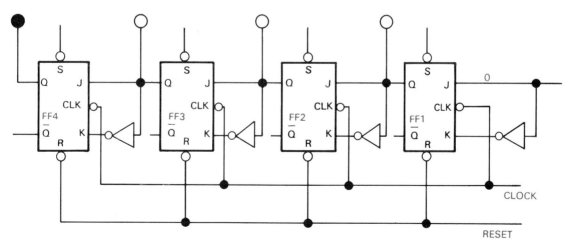

**Figure 8-5.** Serial shift register after the fourth clock pulse

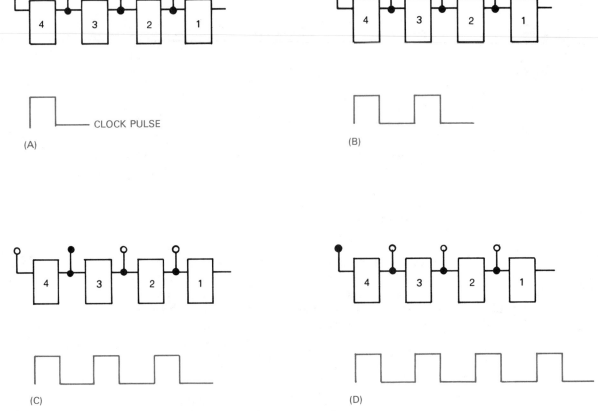

**Figure 8-6.** With each clock pulse, data moves from right to left.

An interesting demonstration with a shift register is binary multiplication and division. For example, if the number 0101 (5) is entered into the shift register in Figure 8-9A and one clock pulse occurs, the number will be multipled by two and will appear as 1010 (10) in Figure 8-9B. On the other hand, if the circuit is rewired to shift left instead of right, the number 0110 (6) will be 0011 (3) after one clock pulse. The number 0110 will have been divided by two.

**PARALLEL-LOAD SHIFT REGISTERS**

*Parallel-load shift registers* are also made up of JK flip-flops; however, the data can be entered into each flip-flop individually through its set inputs. Figure 8-10 shows the schematic design of a parallel-load shift register.

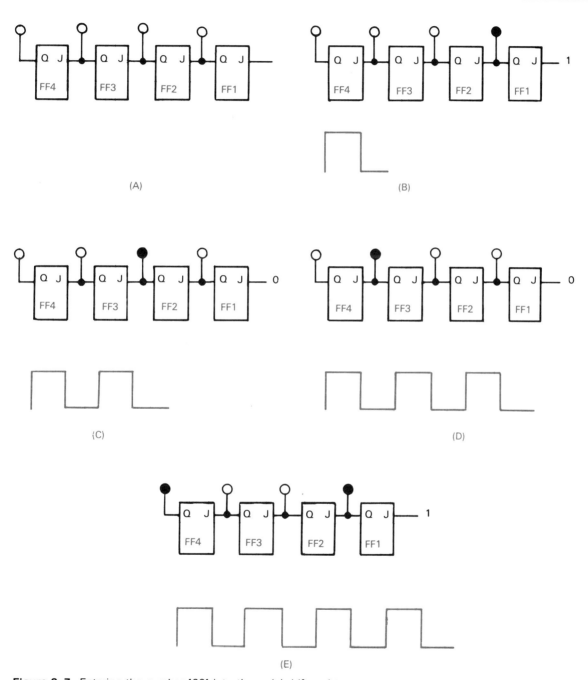

**Figure 8-7.** Entering the number 1001 into the serial shift register

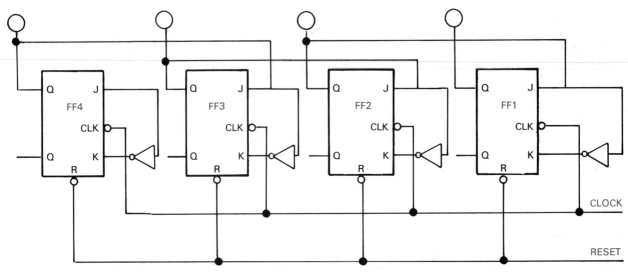

**Figure 8-8.** Serial shift register moving data from left to right

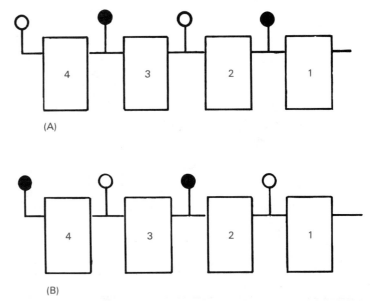

**Figure 8-9.** Multiplication on the shift register. The binary number 0101 in part (A) is multiplied by 2 to give the binary number 1010 in part (B).

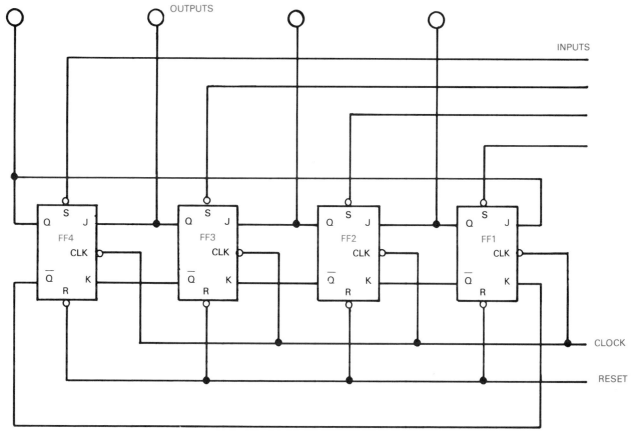

**Figure 8–10.** Parallel-load shift register

To enter the binary number 0011 into the shift register, simply make the inputs of flip-flops 1 and 2 lows (0s). (As you may remember, to make the Q output of a JK flip-flop a 1, the set input must go to a 0 for an instant.) At the first clock pulse the data will be shifted to the left because the J input of FF2 is at 1, and the K input is at 0. The Q of FF2 will stay at 1. FF3 will change to 1 because prior to the clock pulse, input J is 1 because it is connected to the Q of FF2 and K is 0 because it is connected to the $\overline{Q}$ of FF2. FF4 will stay at a 0 because the inputs to J and K are connected to the outputs of FF3.

The second clock pulse will shift the data one more position to the left, making the outputs of FF3 and FF4 1s. The third clock pulse will cause the

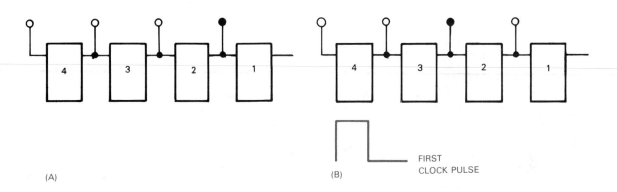

(A)

(B) FIRST CLOCK PULSE

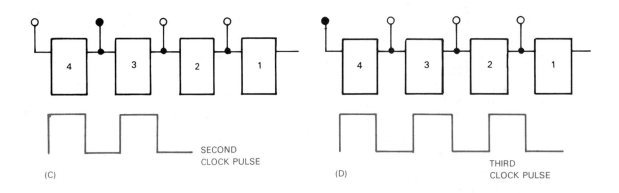

(C) SECOND CLOCK PULSE

(D) THIRD CLOCK PULSE

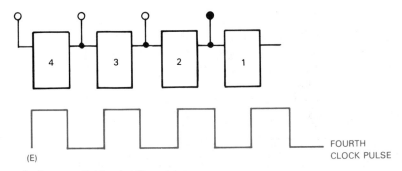

(E) FOURTH CLOCK PULSE

**Figure 8-11.** Data transfer in a parallel-load shift register outputs of FF4 to change FF1 to a 1 because the outputs of FF4 are connected to the inputs of FF1. As more clock pulses occur, the data will appear to shift in a circle through the flip-flops. The data in a parallel-load shift register does not have to be lost, but can be shifted back to its original position every four clock pulses. Figure 8–11 shows data being transferred through the flip-flops.

The parallel-load shift registers have an advantage over the serial-load shift registers. This advantage is that data can be entered into any of the flip-flops individually in a parallel-load shift register rather than having to be shifted from one flip-flop to the next, as in the serial-load shift register.

**COMPARISONS**

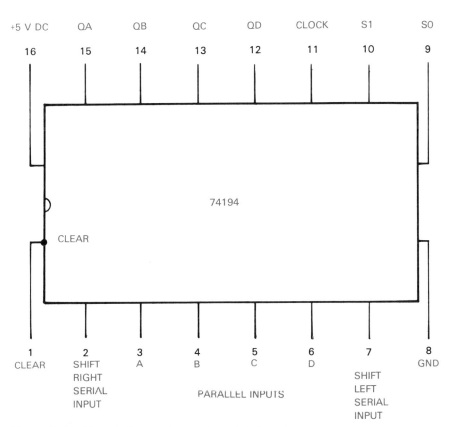

**Figure 8-12.** Pin-out diagram for a universal shift register

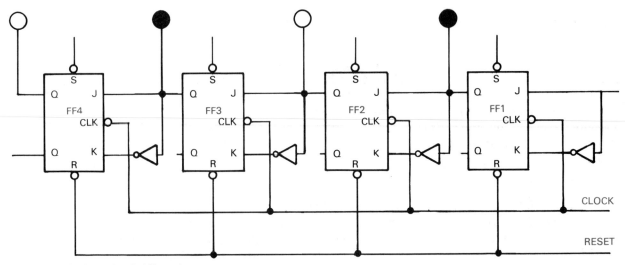

**Figure 8-13.** Serial-load shift register

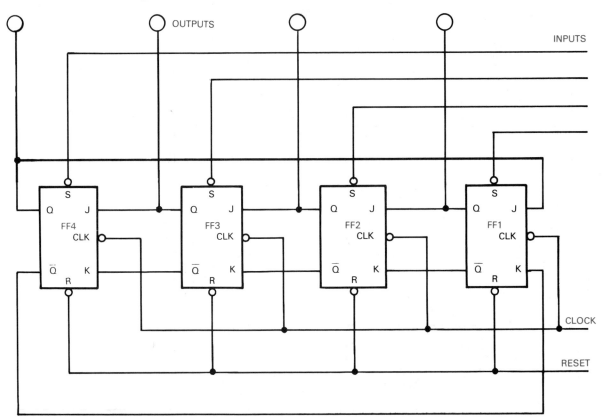

**Figure 8-14.** Parallel-load shift register

As has just been shown, shift registers can be made up of individual flip-flops; however, for most applications, to do so would be very time-consuming and would require considerable space on a circuit board. Therefore, integrated circuits (ICs) are made that combine the necessary flip-flops and logic gates to make various kinds of shift registers.

One IC that is versatile because it can perform as either a serial shift register or as a parallel shift register is the 74194 Universal Shift Register. The pin-out diagram for it appears in Figure 8–12.

Microprocessor chips may contain several shift registers. These are used to temporarily store data before or after it is processed by the microprocessor. The microprocessor can also change the data in these registers.

**SUMMARY**

There are two main types of shift registers—serial load and parallel load. Serial-load shift registers require only one input connection, while parallel-load shift registers have four or more inputs. Data may be shifted either right to left or left to right in shift registers as needed. Shift registers are also used to temporarily store data in calculators. Shift registers are built into special ICs such as the 74194 or directly into microprocessor chips.

# REVIEW QUESTIONS

1. Why are shift registers used in calculators and computers?
2. In the diagram in Figure 8–13, what is the quickest method for making all of the outputs go to 0 without disconnecting the power?
3. What is another method to make all of the outputs 0 in the serial-load shift register of Figure 8–13 (without disconnecting the power)?
4. The binary number in the serial-load shift register in Figure 8–13 is 0101. What would the binary number be after one clock pulse if the J input was kept at 0? After two clock pulses?
5. What would the binary number in the shift register of Figure 8–13 be after one clock pulse if input J was a 1?
6. Draw a wiring diagram that shows how to rewire the circuit in Figure 8–13 to make it shift data to the right.
7. Explain how the binary number 1010 would be entered into the parallel-load shift register of Figure 8–14.
8. If one clock pulse occurred after the binary number 1010 was entered into the parallel-load shift register, what would the binary number be at the outputs?

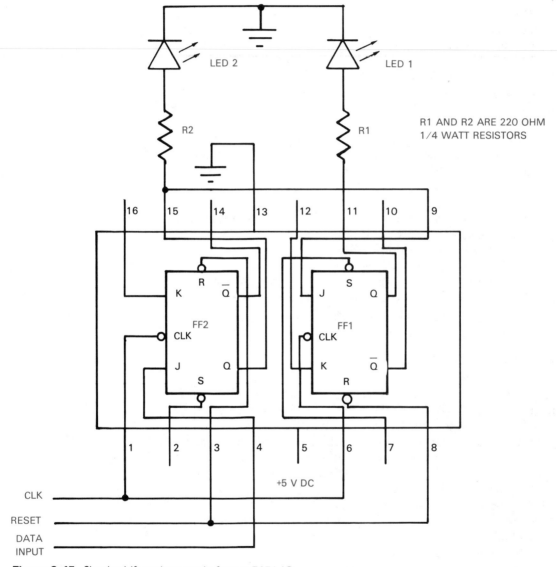

**Figure 8-15.** Simple shift register made from a 7476 IC

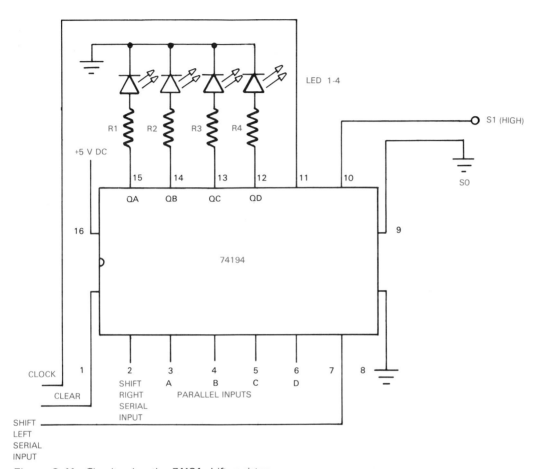

**Figure 8-16.** Circuit using the 74194 shift register

## SUGGESTED ACTIVITIES

1. From the diagram in Figure 8–15, build a simple shift register using the 7476 IC.
2. From the diagram in Figure 8–16, wire up a serial-load shift register that moves data to the left. Use the 74194 IC.

# 9

# COUNTERS

After studying this chapter, you will be able to:
- Make a wiring diagram of a four-bit binary counter.
- Use a counter and make it count backward as well as forward.
- List the advantages and disadvantages of asynchronous counters as compared to synchronous counters.
- Make a wiring diagram that shows how specific numbers can be decoded from a binary counter.
- Make wiring diagrams of specific modulo counters.
- Draw a wiring diagram showing how to cascade decade counters.

## OVERVIEW

Binary counters are used in many electronic circuits such as those in digital watches and advanced computers. In digital watches the counter simply keeps track of the number of electronic pulses. Computers use counters for many operations but especially to keep the sequence of operations in order.

The counter circuit, like that of the shift register, uses flip-flops connected together. The counter circuit, however, produces a sequential (in proper order) count. In computers the counter controls the order of operations. A computer programmer must number all of the steps that the computer is to perform. When the program is entered and the operations begin, a counter inside the computer checks to be certain that one step is completed before allowing the computer to advance to the next operation.

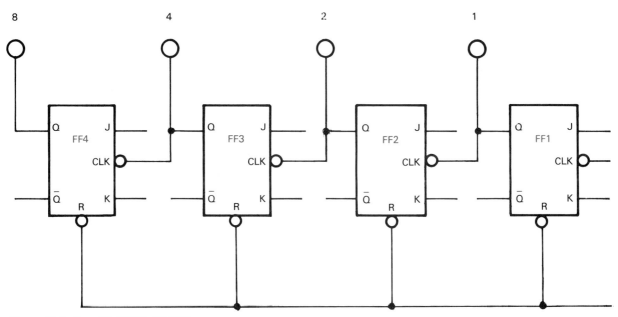

**Figure 9-1.** Four-bit binary counter

Figures 9-1 through 9-7 illustrate steps in the operation of a binary counter as it counts from 0000 (0) to 1111 (15). Because the action of each flip-flop triggers the action of the next, the operation resembles tapping a line of standing dominoes at one end so that they fall, one at a time, each triggering the next. The simple binary counter is an asynchronous counter.

The counter in Figure 9-1 makes use of four flip-flops. The flip-flops are all reset so that the counter starts at 0000, Figure 9-2. Notice in the figure that J and K of FF1 are not connected, however, and that each of the Q outputs is assigned a particular position in a binary number.

After the first full clock pulse, both J and K are 1s (floating highs). Because they are both high, the output at FF1 changes states—in this case from 0 to 1, and the counter indicator goes to 0001. The other flip-flops stay at 0 because their clock inputs are connected to Q outputs of flip-flops 1, 2, and 3, which are at 0, Figure 9-3. (Remember that the outputs of a JK flip-flop do not change when both J and K inputs are at 0). Only when the Q outputs of flip-flops 1, 2, and 3 go from 1 to 0 will the clock inputs of flip-flops 2, 3, and 4 respectively receive a pulse that is going from high to low (trailing edge).

The second clock pulse causes FF1 to return to 0. The action of FF1 going from 1 to 0 provides the negative part of a clock pulse to the clock input of FF2. Since both of its inputs are at 1, it toggles and goes from 0 to 1.

**SIMPLE BINARY COUNTER**

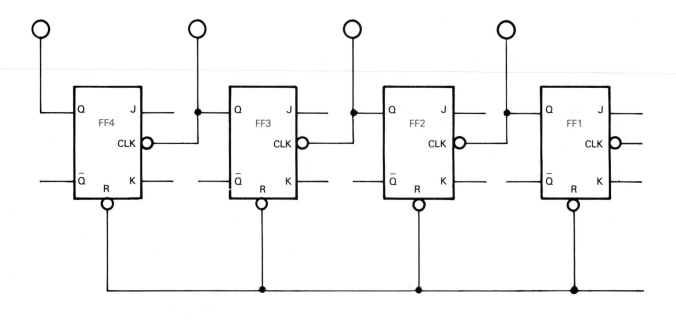

**Figure 9-2.** Binary counter reset to 0

The outputs now appear as a binary number 2, as shown in Figure 9-4.

The third clock pulse simply turns FF1 back on to 1. Since the other flip-flops do not get the negative part of the clock pulse, they do not change. The Q outputs appear as a binary number 3, as shown in Figure 9-5.

Clock pulse number four toggles FF1 to a 0, but as output Q of FF1 goes from 1 to 0, it provides the negative-going clock pulse to FF2, which toggles from 1 to 0. In turn, the Q provides a negative-going clock pulse to FF2, which toggles from 0 to 1, making the Q outputs display a binary number 4, as shown in Figure 9-6.

The next three clock pulses cause flip-flops 1 and 2 to repeat their actions of the first three pulses. Figure 9-7 shows the Q outputs displaying the numbers 5, 6, and 7 in binary.

With the eighth clock pulse, all of the outputs change. FF1 goes back to 0, which causes FF2 to receive a negative-going clock pulse. That pulse toggles FF2 from 1 to 0, which provides a negative-going clock pulse to FF3.

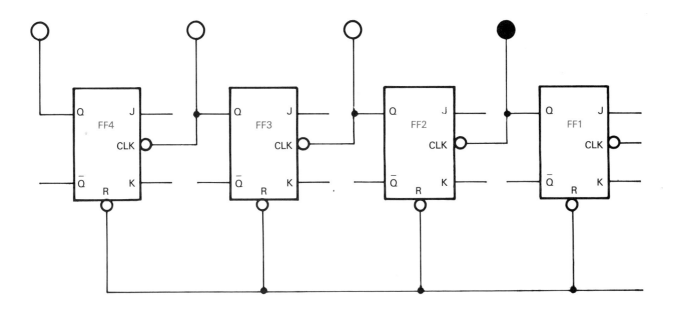

**Figure 9-3.** Binary counter after one clock pulse

The negative pulse toggles FF3 from 1 to 0, providing a negative-going clock pulse to FF4. FF4, in turn, toggles from 0 to 1, leaving the outputs displaying the binary number 8, as shown in Figure 9-8.

The next seven clock pulses are a repeat of the first seven, and the numbers change from 9 through 15. It takes 15 pulses to make the counter display the binary number 15.

The sixteenth clock pulse toggles FF1 back to 0, which starts a chain reaction of the output of the other flip-flops going from 1 to 0. With all of the outputs at 0, the counter starts the count over again at the next clock pulse.

This type of binary counter is called a four-bit *binary ripple counter* because of the ripple effect created by one flip-flop changing output states, which causes the next flip-flop to change states, etc. Although the rippling action is so fast that the outputs appear to change simultaneously, it is still not fast enough for some computer operations in which clock pulses occur in the thousands per second.

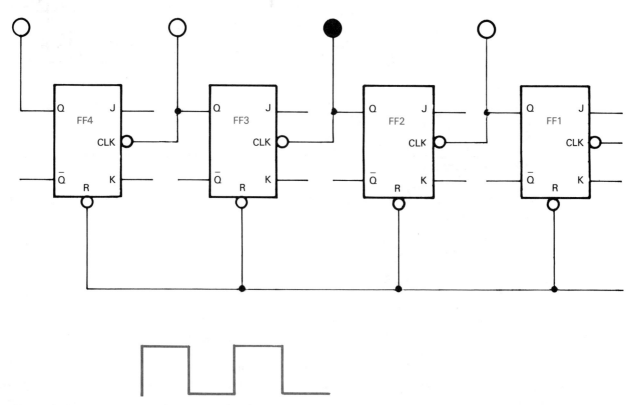

**Figure 9-4.** Binary counter after two clock pulses

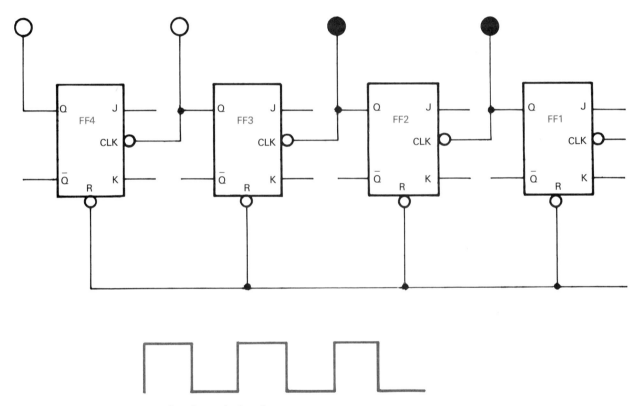

**Figure 9-5.** Binary counter after three clock pulses

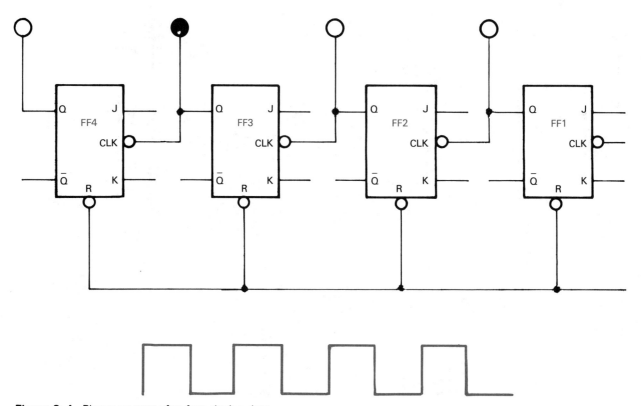

**Figure 9-6.** Binary counter after four clock pulses

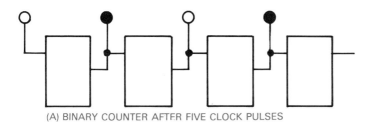

(A) BINARY COUNTER AFTER FIVE CLOCK PULSES

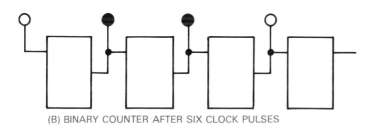

(B) BINARY COUNTER AFTER SIX CLOCK PULSES

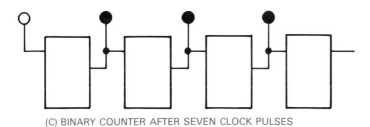

(C) BINARY COUNTER AFTER SEVEN CLOCK PULSES

**Figure 9-7.** Binary counters after five, six, and seven clock pulses

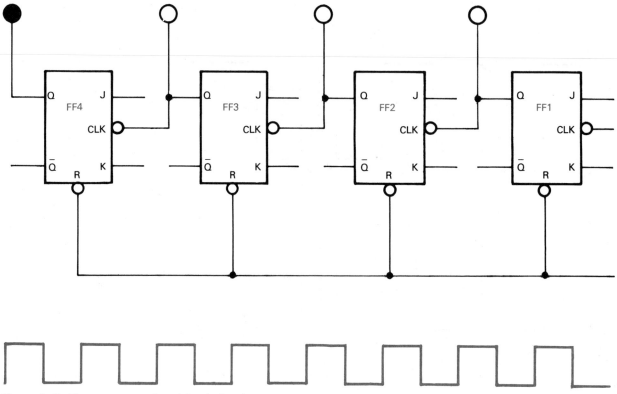

**Figure 9-8.** Binary counter after eight clock pulses

## Pascal

Blaise Pascal was born in France in 1623. He began learning mathematics at age twelve on his own and by age sixteen wrote an essay on conic sections that was received with great admiration from respected mathematicians of that time. In order to help his father, who had been appointed as a local administrator to do tax computations, Pascal invented a calculating machine. This machine was easy to operate and could add, subtract, multiply, and divide. It could also carry digits over to the next column and record totals. This calculating device was apparently the first digital calculator.

Pascal discovered and documented many principles of mathematics and made some important discoveries in the field of physics. He also became a great religious philosopher and writer. Pascal died in 1662.

Blaise Pascal (courtesy of IBM Corporation)

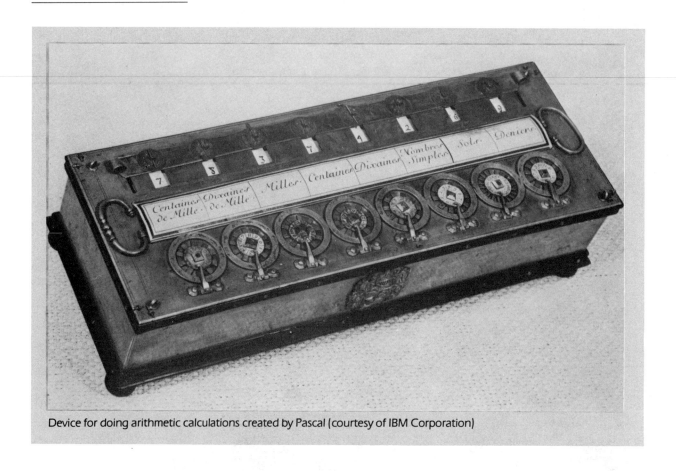

Device for doing arithmetic calculations created by Pascal (courtesy of IBM Corporation)

**DOWN COUNTER**     The *down counter* gets its name from the fact that it will count backward. It is easily made from the simple binary counter by changing the connection to the clock of flip-flops 2, 3, and 4 from the Q to $\overline{Q}$.

Figure 9–9 shows a four-bit down counter. With the outputs set at 1, the counter displays the binary number 1111 (15). The next clock pulse toggles FF1 back to 0, but since $\overline{Q}$ goes from 0 to 1, there is not a negative-going clock pulse to FF2. Thus, FF2 is unaffected, and the counter displays 1110 (14).

The next clock pulse toggles FF1 back to 1, causing Q to change from 1 to 0. This change gives a negative-going clock pulse to FF2, which causes its Q output to toggle from 1 to 0. Because the FF2's $\overline{Q}$ is changing from 0 to 1, FF3 is not affected, and the counter displays the binary number 1101 (13). This process continues until the counter reaches 0000. Then all of the flip-flops are toggled to 1s, and the count starts over again.

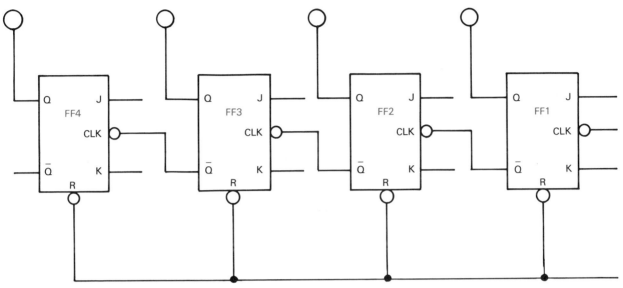

**Figure 9-9.** Four-bit down counter. This counter counts backward from 15 to 0, then recycles.

Countdown times are used for timing athletic events where the period of play is a particular length of time. The timer is set to the allotted time and counts down to zero.

## SYNCHRONOUS COUNTER

The *synchronous counter* is used in computers because it is much faster than either the simple binary counter or the down counter. All of the flip-flops receive the clock pulse at the same instant, and any changes in outputs occur simultaneously. Each flip-flop must have the proper inputs before the next clock pulse occurs. To insure having the proper inputs, simple logic gates are placed between flip-flops. Figure 9-10 shows a synchronous counter.

The first flip-flop is again allowed to toggle with each clock pulse because both inputs are in the floating high (1) condition.

After the first clock pulse, FF1's Q output is a 1. Since J and K of FF2 are both connected to the Q of FF1, they are both at 1, so the second clock pulse will make Q output of FF2 toggle to a 1. (Before the clock pulse, it was at 0.) FF1 returns to a 0 at the second clock pulse, and the counter shows 0010.

The third clock pulse simply allows output Q of FF1 to go back to a 1. The other FFs are unchanged by the third clock pulse because their J and K inputs are at 0. The counter reads 0011. Ony when both Q outputs of FF1 and FF2 are a 1 does the AND gate they are connected to have a 1 output. The 1 at the output of this AND gate is connected to J and K input of FF3. At

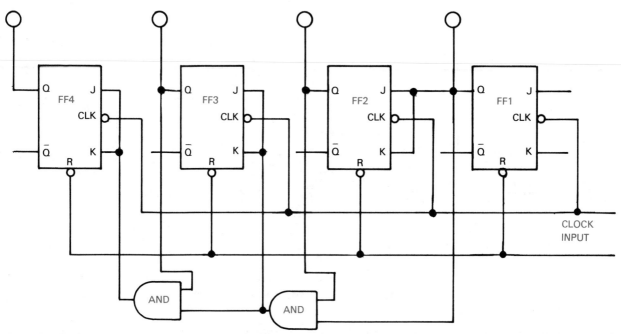

**Figure 9–10.** Synchronous counter. All flip-flops receive clock pulse at the same time and change state at the same time.

the fourth clock pulse, FF3 toggles to a 1. FF2 and FF1 both toggle back to 0 and counters reads 0100.

FF3 remains at 1 for four clock pulses—4, 5, 6, and 7. It toggles back to 0 only on the clock pulse that occurs after flip-flops 1 and 2 are both at 1 again, which occurs at the count of 7.

FF4 is caused to toggle only when flip-flops 1, 2, and 3 are at 1 because they provide the three high inputs needed to get a 1 output from the three-input AND gate. The output of the three-input AND gate is connected to the J and K of FF4. FF4 toggles at the number 7 and at the number 15.

Figure 9–11 illustrates how FF1 toggles on every clock pulse, FF2 after two clock pulses, FF3 after four clock pulses, and FF4 only after eight clock pulses.

**DECODING COUNTER**        Instead of controlling the next flip-flop in a counting circuit, the output of a gate connected to a counter can control external devices such as an electric motor, etc. A counter used in this way is called a *decoding counter*. In decoding counters both the Q and $\overline{Q}$ (not Q) outputs of some of the flip-flops provide the specific inputs needed to decode certain numbers. Outputs of 1 are needed from the flip-flops of a counter to provide inputs

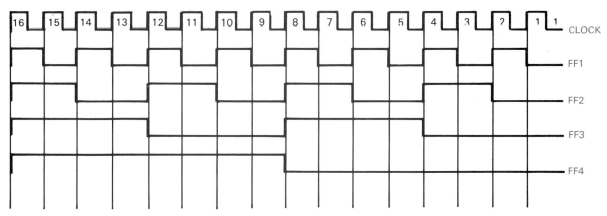

**Figure 9-11.** How clock pulses affect toggle action of flip-flops in a binary counter.

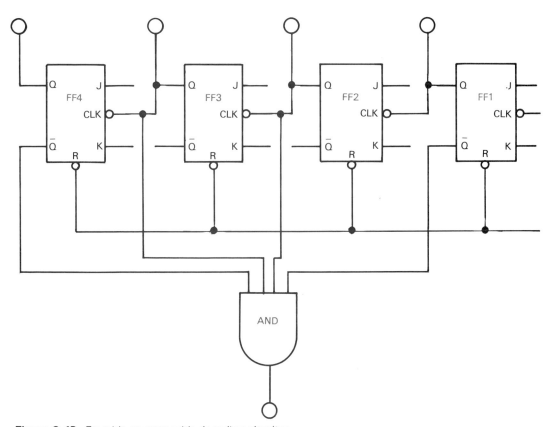

**Figure 9-12.** Four-bit counter with decoding circuitry

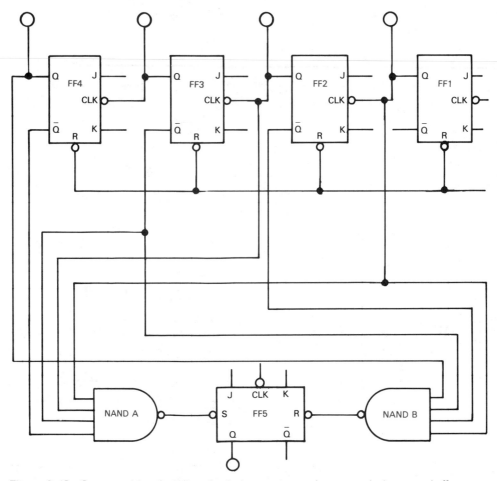

**Figure 9–13.** Counter with a decoding circuit that can be used to turn a device on and off

that will make the output of the AND gate 1. It is practical to use $\overline{Q}$ (not Q) outputs of some of the flip-flops to decode certain numbers.

The circuit in Figure 9–12 shows Q outputs and $\overline{Q}$ outputs being used to decode the number 6. As you can see, the Q outputs of flip-flops 1 and 4 are 0 at the number 6, but the $\overline{Q}$ outputs are 1s. Therefore, the $\overline{Q}$ outputs are connected along with the Q outputs of FF2 and FF3 to provide the four 1 inputs needed at the AND gate to make its output a 1.

An interesting circuit that can be used to turn on a device at a certain number and shut it off at a different number appears in Figure 9–13. The number 3 is decoded by the NAND gate A. The 0 it provides to the "set" of FF5 only when all of its inputs are at 1 causes the Q output of FF5 to be a 1. At the number 9, NAND gate B has 1s at all of its inputs and thus provides a 0 to the reset of FF5, which causes its output to go back to 0. This type of circuit could be used in a computer-controlled milling machine to regulate the fluid that is used to cool the cutter. The fluid would be turned on at step 3 of the process and turned off when step 9 starts.

Counters can not only be decoded to operate a device at a certain count, but they can also be decoded to stop counting at a certain count. For example, to stop a four-bit binary counter at binary number 1100 (12), the circuit in Figure 9–14 may be used. The binary number 12 is decoded by connecting the inputs of the NAND gate to the Qs of flip-flops 3 and 4. When both Qs are 1s, which does not happen until the count has reached 12, the output of the NAND gate goes to 0. The output of the NAND gate makes J and K of FF1 0, and no change occurs in that flip-flop. Since FF1 controls the other flip-flops, the count is stopped until the counter has been reset. The four-bit binary counter counts from 0 to 15 and then starts over, but often counters are needed that can count to other numbers.

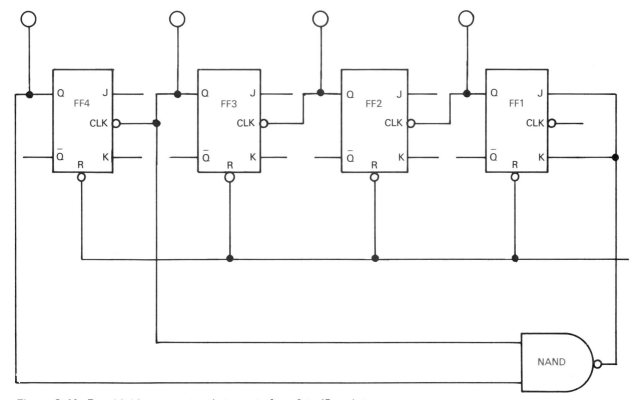

**Figure 9–14.** Four-bit binary counter that counts from 0 to 12 and stops

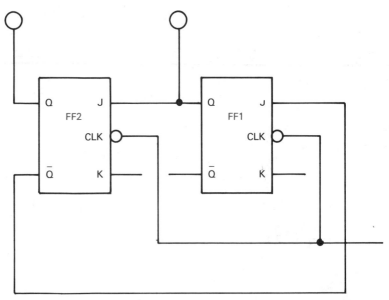

**Figure 9-15.** Synchronous binary counter that counts to 2 and recycles to 0

## MODULO COUNTER

There are several ways to design counters to count to numbers other than 1, 2, 4, 8, 16, etc. For example, you can make a counter that will count only three counts (0, 1, 2) from two flip-flops, just as you would a counter that counts to four, except that you must change some connections that cause the counter to automatically recycle to 0 after the binary number 2.

Figure 9-15 shows a synchronous counter that recycles to 0 after the number 2 in binary because the 0 at Q of FF2 is connected back to the J input of FF1. A 0 at the J input and 1 at the K input (floating high) cause Q of FF1 to stay at 0. The 0 at Q of FF1 connected to the J input of FF2 plus the 1 at the K input of FF2 (floating high) cause Q of FF2 to recycle back to 0. This counter is called a *mod (modulo) counter* because it counts in modules of a predetermined value.

Now that a counter that can count to 3 instead of 1, 2, 4, 8, etc., has been developed, possibilities for other counters have been created. By connecting another flip-flop to the mod-3 counter, a mod-6 counter can be made. The mod-3 counter toggles (changes) the next flip-flop each time its count goes from 2 to 0. After the first three clock pulses, the mod-3 counter is back to 0, but the flip-flop has to change from 0 to 1. After three more clock pulses, both the flip-flop and the mod-3 counter recycle to 0 completing the count to 6. Figure 9-16 shows a circuit that will count six clock pulses, then recycle. However, if you examine the Q outputs

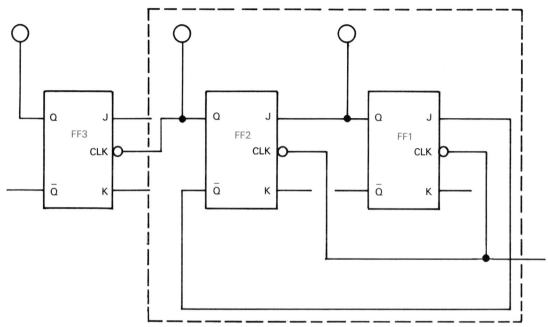

**Figure 9-16.** Mod-6 counter made by connecting a mod-3 counter to a JK flip-flop

throughout the count, you see that the counter goes 0, 1, 2, 4, 5, 6, and back to 0, skipping the number 3. This condition can be corrected by putting the flip-flop ahead of the mod-3 counter so that the flip-flop provides the clock pulse for the mod-3 counter, as shown in Figure 9-17. Follow through the same count of six clock pulses in Figure 9-17 to see that the count stays in order from 0 through 5 and back to 0. This counter is called a mod-6 counter.

By adding another flip-flop in front of the mod-6 counter, a mod-12 counter as shown in Figure 9-18 can be made. With just one more flip-flop a time-clock that counts to 12 A.M., recycles the mod-12 counter, then counts to 12 P.M. can be made. The flip-flop on the output (end) of the mod-12 counter keeps track of the A.M. and P.M., Figure 9-19.

The most popular modulo counter is the *decade counter*. The fact that it counts 10 pulses and then recycles makes it ideal to use with decimal (base 10) numbers in digital thermometers, gasoline pumps, pressure gauges, etc. There are several ways to make a binary counter recycle after 10 pulses. Figure 9-20 shows one method. Because the decade counter is

**DECADE COUNTER**

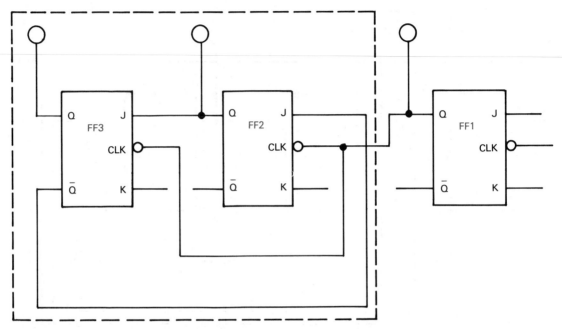

**Figure 9-17.** Mod-6 counter that counts from 0 through 5 and recycles

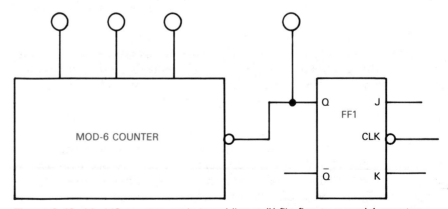

**Figure 9-18.** Mod-12 counter made by adding a JK flip-flop to a mod-6 counter

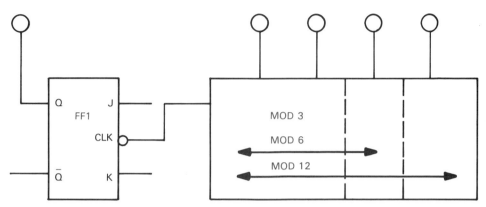

**Figure 9-19.** Mod-12 binary counter with additional JK flip-flop can show A.M. and P.M. when used as a clock

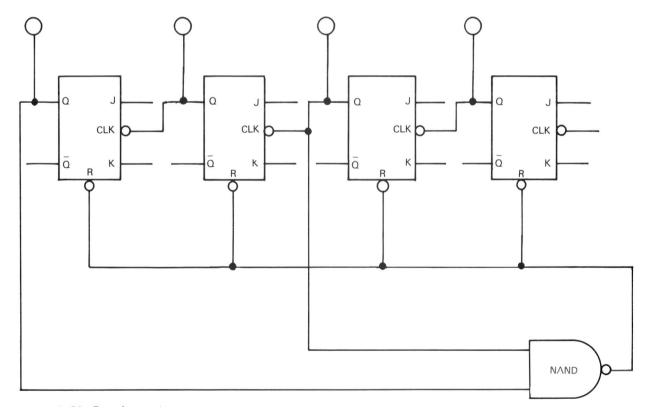

**Figure 9-20.** Decade counter

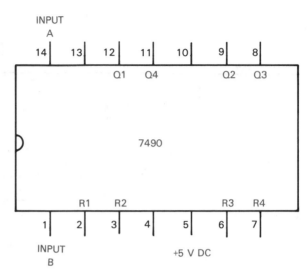

**Figure 9-21.** Pin-out diagram for a 7490 decade counter

popular, a digital IC containing a decade counter is available. It is the 7490, and a pin-out diagram of it is shown in Figure 9-21.

Another type of counter that is available is the 74193, shown in Figure 9-22. The 74193, a four-bit binary counter, is also a synchronous counter because all of the flip-flops receive the clock pulse at the same time. It can also be either an up counter or a down counter by simply changing the inputs to either pin 4 or pin 5. Pin 14 allows the counter to be cleared whenever it is desired. Inputs 1, 9, 10, and 15 can be set to a desired binary number. Whenever a 0 is applied to pin 11, the counter automatically goes to the binary number programmed into pins 1, 9, 10, and 15. For example, the counter could be changed so that instead of counting to 15 and then recycling back to 0 (mod-16 counter), it would recycle back to 3 when it reached 15. (If this were the case, it would be a mod-12 counter.) To make such a change, pin 15 data input A would have to be connected to a 1, pin 1 data input B to a 1, and pin 10 data input C to a 0 and pin 9 data input D to a 0, Figure 9-23.

To make pin 11 (LOAD) go to a 0 to reset the counter to 3 (the number programmed into the data inputs), a four-input NAND gate could be connected to the outputs of the counter on the twelfth clock pulse. All of the outputs would be high for the binary number 15, and the output from the NAND gate would be 0. The output of the NAND gate would be connected to pin 11 (LOAD), which would cause the counter to immediately recycle to the number 3, in effect skipping the binary number 15.

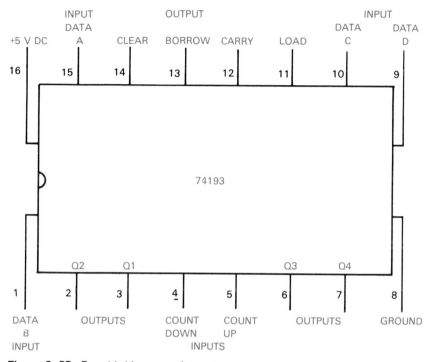

**Figure 9-22.** Four-bit binary up-down counter

Figure 9-23 shows that only when all of the outputs are at 1 (binary 15), does the NAND gate put a 0 to pin 11 (LOAD). Pin 14 is used to clear the outputs (reset them to 0) when a 1 is applied to it. The clear function operates independently from count and load inputs.

This counter can also be connected directly to other counters without external circuitry to count beyond 16 pulses. (This process is called *cascading.*) Pin 12 (carry) provides a pulse to pin 5 (count up) of the next counter whenever the counter recycles back to 0. Pin 13 (borrow) provides a pulse to pin 4 (countdown) of the next counter whenever the counter in the countdown mode goes from 0 back to 15. Figure 9-24A shows two counters cascaded to count up, and Figure 9-24B shows two counters cascaded to count down.

JK flip-flops are commonly used as *frequency dividers.* Frequency dividers are used in time-keeping devices such as digital clocks. Since a flip-flop with both J and K at 1 toggles with each clock pulse, its Q output

**FREQUENCY DIVIDER**

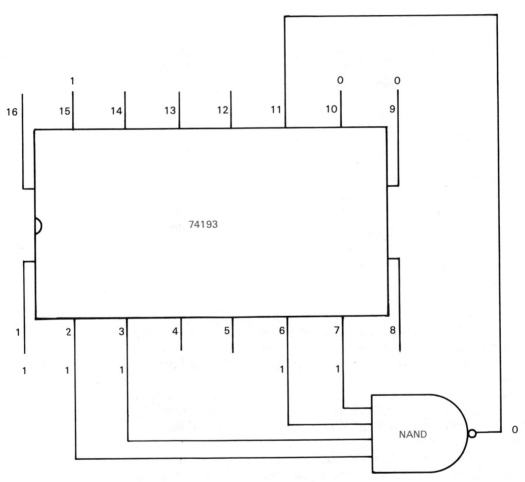

**Figure 9-23.** Four-bit binary up-down counter programmed to count between 3 and 15 and recycle

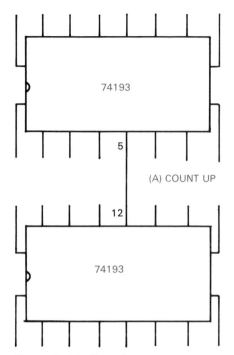

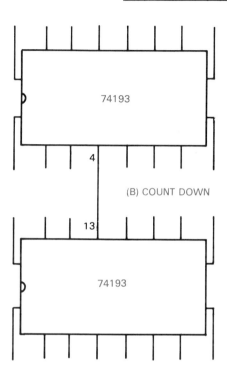

**Figure 9-24.** Cascading counters

creates one pulse for every two clock pulses. The trailing edge of one clock pulse makes the Q output go high; the next clock pulse makes it go low to complete a cycle. Therefore, the incoming frequency is divided in half. Because each flip-flop divides the frequency in half, several flip-flops may be connected in line to reduce a high frequency to a low frequency.

An example of how the frequency can be divided is given in Figure 9–25. Frequency is measured in cycles per second. The term *hertz* (Hz) is used to mean "cycles per second." After passing through one flip-flop, a frequency of 10,000 Hz is divided by two, resulting in a frequency of 5000 Hz. After the second flip-flop, the frequency is 2500 Hz, etc.

**SUMMARY**

In this chapter you learned that JK flip-flops work very well as components in counter circuits. Of the two types of counters discussed, asynchronous counters are slower but simpler than synchronous counters. Synchronous counters are faster because the flip-flops all receive clock pulses at the same time so they can all change states at the same time. In asynchronous counters each flip-flop must wait until the flip-flop in front of

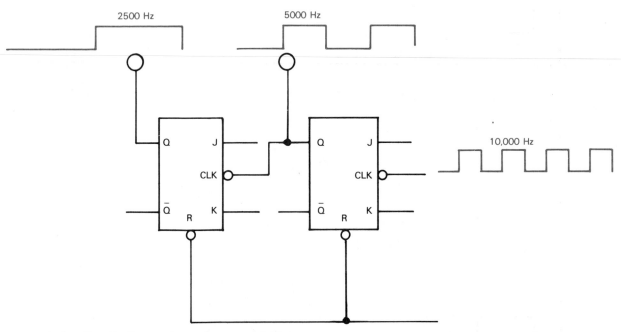

**Figure 9–25.** Two flip-flops acting as frequency dividers

it changes states to create the clock pulse for it. Counters can also be made to count any number of clock pulses before they recycle, or they can be made to stop at a certain clock pulse. They are also useful for dividing high frequencies into lower frequencies.

## REVIEW QUESTIONS

1. Which counter is faster—asynchronous or synchronous? Explain why one is faster than the other.
2. What number is decoded at the output of the AND gate in the counter circuit shown in Figure 9–26?
3. In the circuit of Figure 9–27, at what number will the output of the JK flip-flop go to 1? At what number will the output return to a 0?
4. If the counter in Figure 9–28 started at 0000, at what number will it stop?

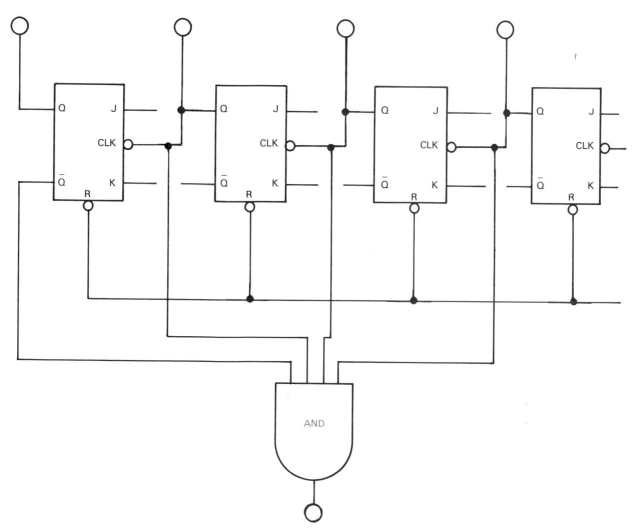

**Figure 9–26.** Four-bit counter with decoding circuitry

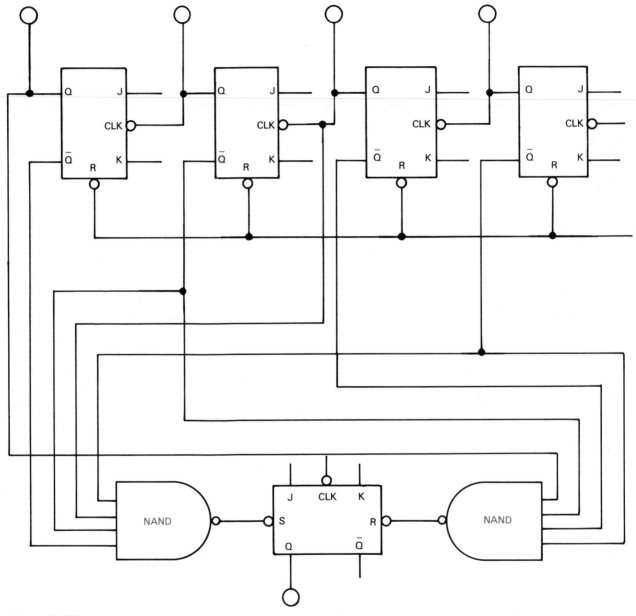

**Figure 9-27**

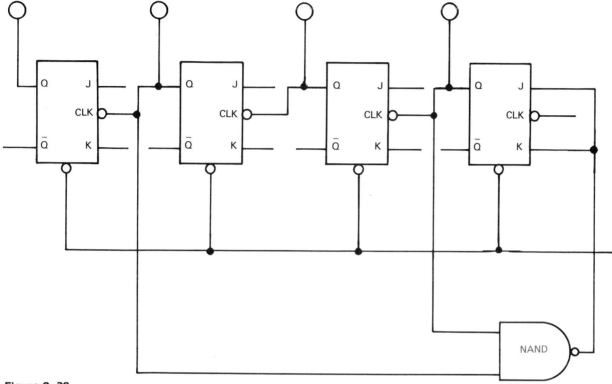

Figure 9-28

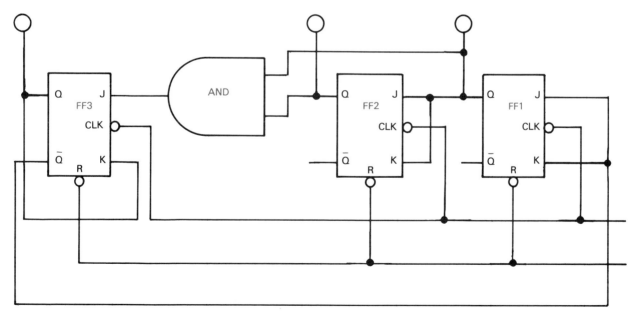

Figure 9-29

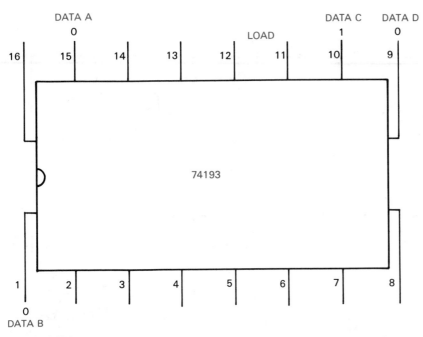

Figure 9-30

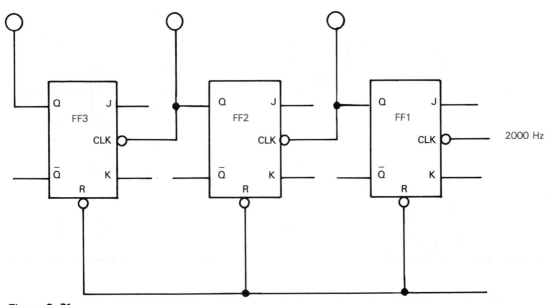

Figure 9-31

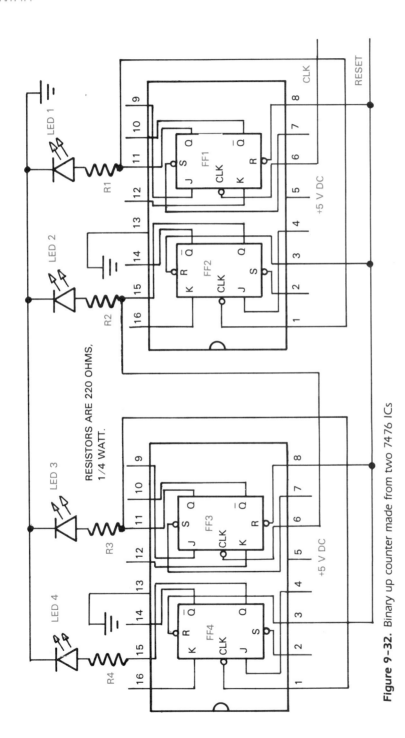

**Figure 9-32.** Binary up counter made from two 7476 ICs

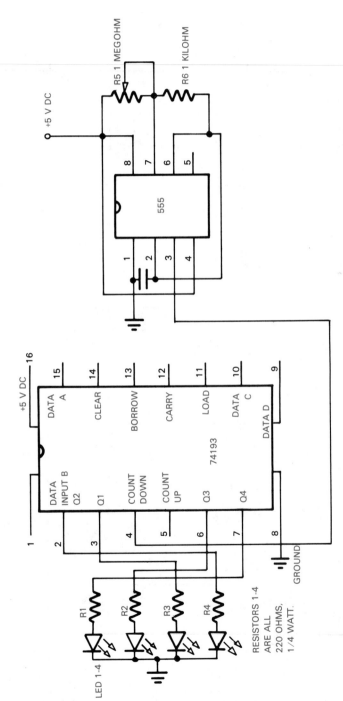

**Figure 9-33.** 74193 being used as a down counter

5. The counter in Figure 9-29 is a modulo counter. How many clock pulses does it count? It is helpful to start at 0 and record what happens to the output of each flip-flop after each clock pulse, i.e.:

|       | C | B | A |
|-------|---|---|---|
| Start | 0 | 0 | 0 |
| 1st   | . | . | . |
| 2nd   | . | . | . |
| etc.  |   |   |   |

6. What number will the 74193 in Figure 9-30 recycle to when a 0 is put to pin 11?
7. To make the 74193 count up, should pin 4 or 5 be at 0?
8. What would the frequency be at the output of flip-flop 3 in Figure 9-31?

## SUGGESTED ACTIVITIES

1. Wire the circuit in Figure 9-32 to make an up counter.
2. Using a 74193 in place of the 7476s in Figure 9-32, wire the circuit in Figure 9-33 to make a countdown counter.

# 10

# CODING AND DECODING

## OBJECTIVES

After studying this chapter, you will be able to:
- Count in special codes used by computers such as BCD and Gray code.
- Encode numbers from a standard keyboard to binary.
- Decode numbers from binary to a seven-segment display.
- Convert data from several inputs to one data line.
- Demultiplex data from a data line.

## OVERVIEW

Because counting in binary gets more difficult as the numbers get larger, various methods have been developed to make the binary system easier to understand and use. One method of simplifying the binary system is to use some form of binary coded decimal (BCD).

In this chapter you will learn about the most often used binary coded decimal system and another system called the Gray code. You will also learn how computers communicate with each other all around the world over a few transmission lines by combining data at the sending end and separating it at the receiving end. These processes of combining and separating data are called multiplexing and demultiplexing.

| DECIMAL | BINARY | BCD |
|---------|--------|-----|
| 0 | 0000 | 0000 |
| 1 | 0001 | 0001 |
| 2 | 0010 | 0010 |
| 3 | 0011 | 0011 |
| 4 | 0100 | 0100 |
| 5 | 0101 | 0101 |
| 6 | 0110 | 0110 |
| 7 | 0111 | 0111 |
| 8 | 1000 | 1000 |
| 9 | 1001 | 1001 |

**Figure 10-1.** Comparison of number systems for the decimal numbers 0 through 9

**BINARY CODED DECIMAL**

There are many kinds of *binary coded decimals* (BCD), but since the 8421 is used the most, it is usually referred to as the *BCD* code. In the BCD code, the digits from 0 to 9 are just the same as in the binary system. Figure 10-1 compares the numbers 0 to 9 in the BCD, decimal, and binary systems.

Following 9, an additional four-bit number is used in a column to the left of the first one to indicate tens value. As you can see from Figure 10-2, the number 20 is much easier to recognize in BCD than in pure binary. The BCD system makes dealing with large numbers easier and faster because you have to be able to recognize only the binary numbers 0000-1001.

| DECIMAL | BINARY | BCD |
|---------|--------|-----|
| 9 | 1001 | 1001 |
| 10 | 1010 | 0001 0000 |
| 11 | 1011 | 0001 0001 |
| 12 | 1100 | 0001 0010 |
| 13 | 1101 | 0001 0011 |
| 14 | 1110 | 0001 0100 |
| 15 | 1111 | 0001 0101 |
| 16 | 10000 | 0001 0110 |
| 17 | 10001 | 0001 0111 |
| 18 | 10010 | 0001 1000 |
| 19 | 10010 | 0001 1001 |
| 20 | 10100 | 0010 0000 |

**Figure 10-2.** Comparison of number systems for the decimal numbers 9 through 20

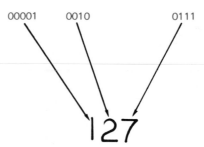

**Figure 10-3.** Binary coded decimal
converted to a decimal number

For numbers larger than 99, an additional column to the left indicates 100s values, and for numbers larger than 999, another column to the left indicates 1000s, etc. Convert the BCD number 0001 0010 0111 to a decimal and compare your answer with the one in Figure 10-3.

**GRAY CODE**

The *Gray code* does not make the binary number system easier to use, nor does it work well for doing arithmetic operations, but it is effectively used with input and output devices. Examples of input and output devices are printers, monitors, keyboards, and joy sticks.

The most noticeable difference between BCD codes and the Gray code is that only one digit changes during the count. Also, digits do not represent place values, as in the 8421 BCD code.

Figure 10-4 shows the decimal, binary, and Gray code numbers from 0 through 15. Notice that in the Gray code, between any number and the next larger or smaller number only one digit changes. For example, the number 8 is 1100, and only the far right digit changes to make the number 9 (1101). Likewise, the number 7 has only the digit to the far left changed from the number 8.

In computers and other electronic devices, electronic decoders are used to make the change from binary to Gray code. The following steps show how the binary can be changed to Gray code manually.

1. To change binary 1001 to Gray code, keep the digit farthest to the left as the most significant bit *(MSB)*, Figure 10-5.
2. Add together the pair of digits farthest to the left and drop the carry. The sum becomes the second digit from the left, as shown in Figure 10-6.
3. Repeat the process of adding pairs of digits by adding the next pair (in this case, the two middle digits) and dropping the carry if there is

| DECIMAL | BINARY | GRAY CODE |
|---------|--------|-----------|
| 0 | 0000 | 0000 |
| 1 | 0001 | 0001 |
| 2 | 0010 | 0011 |
| 3 | 0011 | 0010 |
| 4 | 0100 | 0110 |
| 5 | 0101 | 0111 |
| 6 | 0110 | 0101 |
| 7 | 0111 | 0100 |
| 8 | 1000 | 1100 |
| 9 | 1001 | 1101 |
| 10 | 1010 | 1111 |
| 11 | 1011 | 1110 |
| 12 | 1100 | 1010 |
| 13 | 1101 | 1011 |
| 14 | 1110 | 1001 |
| 15 | 1111 | 1000 |
| ••• | ••• | ••• |

**Figure 10-4.** Decimal, binary, and Gray code number systems

**Figure 10-5.** First step in converting a binary number to Gray code

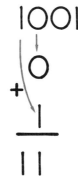

**Figure 10-6.** Second step in converting a binary number to Gray code

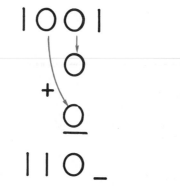

**Figure 10-7.** Third step in converting a binary number to Gray code

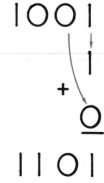

**Figure 10-8.** Final step in converting a binary number to Gray code

any, as shown in Figure 10-7. The sum becomes the third digit from the left.

4. Finally, add the pair of digits on the right, Figure 10-8. This sum makes the last digit on the right; it is referred to as the least significant bit or *LSB*. Remember to drop any carry.

Try changing the binary number 1100 to Gray code. Check your work with the example in Figure 10-9.

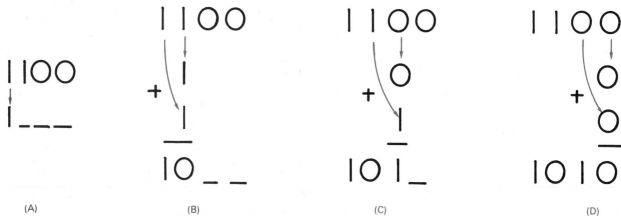

(A)　　　　(B)　　　　(C)　　　　(D)

**Figure 10-9.** Changing the binary number 1100 to Gray code

*Multiplexers* are a group of logic gates that can take several inputs and output them one at a time through one output line. They are often compared to a rotary switch that can connect many circuits one at a time, as shown in Figure 10-10. Multiplexers are sometimes called data selectors because they can take data from one of many inputs and connect it to one output.

A common multiplexer that is built into an integrated circuit is the 74150. It has sixteen data inputs and four data selects. The four data selects are labeled ABCD and are weighted as binary numbers, as shown in Figure 10-11.

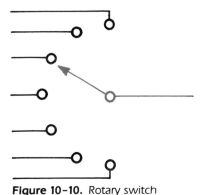

**Figure 10-10.** Rotary switch

**Figure 10-11.** Diagram of 74150 IC illustrating how the four data selects are weighted

By connecting the data selects to the Q outputs of four flip-flops of a four-bit counter, you can select any number between 0 and 15. Any one of the sixteen data inputs can have its data (1 or 0) transferred to the output of the multiplexer simply by setting the four-bit counter to the number of that input. Figure 10-12 shows the four-bit counter set at the number 5 and the data (in this case a 1) being transferred from input number 5 to the output of the multiplexer.

A *demultiplexer* reverses the operation of the multiplexer. It takes data from one input and connects it to one of sixteen outputs. If the counter in Figure 10-13 were connected to a demultiplexer, the data (1) could be transferred to any output of the demultiplexer. However, the data must be put through an inverter to be back in the proper state. In Figure 10-13, the data from the multiplexer is being transferred to output number 5 of the demultiplexer.

The advantage of using multiplexers and demultiplexers to transfer data is apparent in Figure 10-13—only five lines are needed to transfer the data from sixteen inputs to sixteen outputs. Four are data-select lines, and one is a line to complete the circuit. If a sixth line were added, data from thirty-two inputs could be transferred to thirty-two outputs. Five lines would be data selects, and one line would be a line to complete the circuit. As more data-select lines are added between the multiplexer and demultiplexer, the number of inputs and outputs increases rapidly. For example, if there were eight data-select lines, 255 inputs and outputs could be connected, Figure 10-14.

The multiplexer and demultiplexer take data that is in parallel at the inputs of the multiplexer and transfer it serially (one bit follows another) to the demultiplexer, where it is put back into parallel again at the outputs. The speed at which the data is transferred from the multiplexer to the demultiplexer depends upon how fast the counter operates. The faster the clock driving the counter, the more data that can be transferred in a given amount of time.

The pin-out diagrams for the 74150 multiplexer and 74154 demultiplexer appear in Figure 10-15 and Figure 10-16. The small circles at the sixteen outputs of the 74154 (demultiplexer) show that the outputs are actually inverted from the inputs. However, by attaching inverters to the outputs, the data can be changed back to the proper form.

Multiplexers and demultiplexers can be used to transfer computer data which is already in digital and also audio and video information that has been changed into digital form. Used in telephone communications, multiplexers and demultiplexers allow numerous conversations to take place all at the same time on one telephone line rather than having the line restricted to one conversation as was the case in the past.

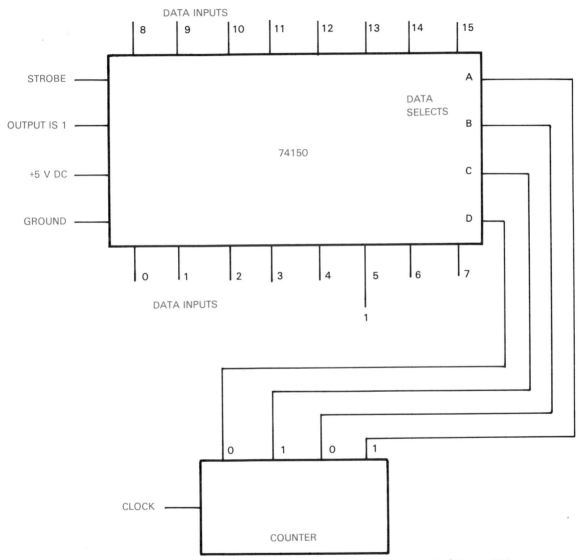

**Figure 10-12.** Multiplexer. The data from input 5 is being transferred to the output of the multiplexer.

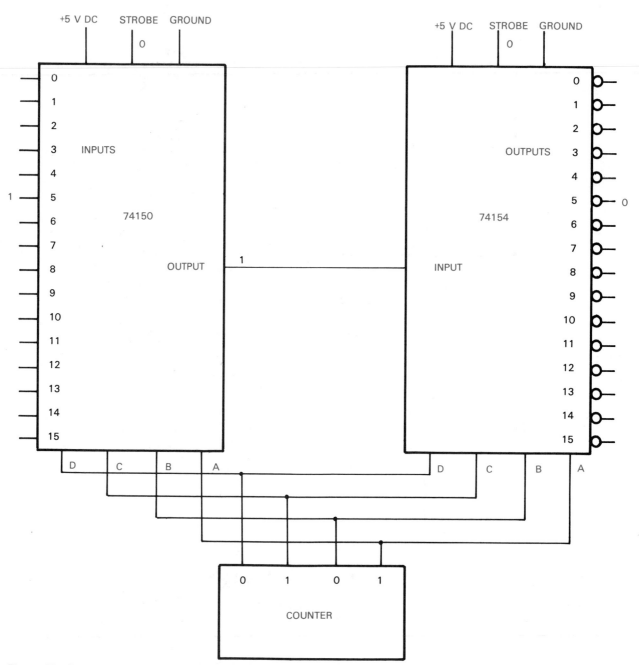

**Figure 10-13.** Multiplexer transferring data to a demultiplexer

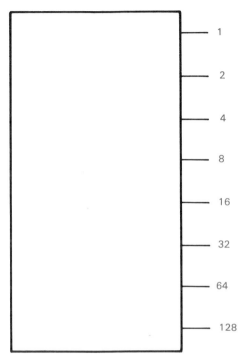

1

2

4

8

16

32

64

128

**Figure 10-14.** Diagram of multiplexer showing the number of inputs possible with eight data-select lines

**ENCODERS**

*Encoding* is the process of electronically changing some code or number system into binary. For example, the keyboard on a calculator changes decimal numbers into binary numbers. Commands given to computers must also be changed to binary numbers before the computers can process the information as desired.

Figure 10-17 shows a 74147 IC that encodes ten inputs (sometimes called lines) to four outputs. As you can see, the 74147 has nine inputs which could be connected to the keys numbered one through nine on a decimal keypad. The four outputs are connected so that they will equal a four-bit binary number. When any of the numbers on the keypad is pushed, the 74147 decodes that input into the proper binary number. When none of the numbers on the keypad is pushed, there are no inputs to the 74147, and the output is a 0. This condition acts as the tenth input or line. By using more complex circuitry, you can encode letters of the alphabet, words, and computer commands into binary numbers.

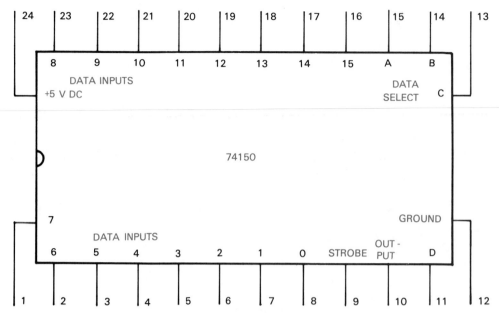

**Figure 10-15.** Pin-out diagram for a 74150 multiplexer

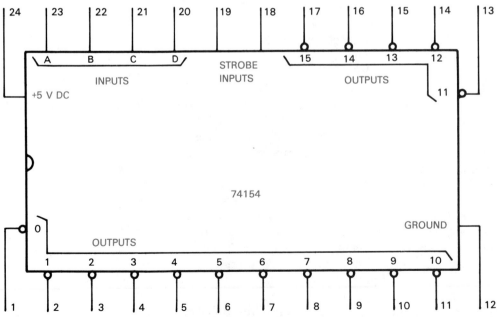

**Figure 10-16.** Pin-out diagram for a 74154 demultiplexer

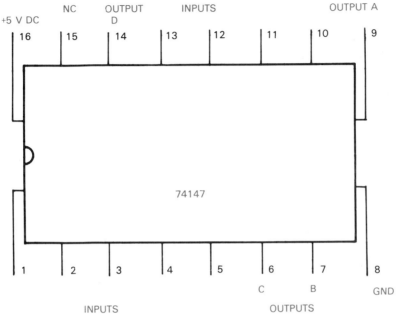

**Figure 10-17.** Encoder with ten inputs and four outputs

## Medical Equipment

Digital electronic computers are making a difference in medical treatment. One such device is a computerized perfusion controller designed and built by Cobe Laboratories. The computerized perfusion controller is used to monitor several areas of concern during open heart surgery.

Multiple temperature sensors, pressure monitors, and cardiac index are a few of the critical life signs that are monitored. Their status is either displayed on the screen or on digital readouts. Three digital timers operate independently to show hours, minutes, and seconds in an easy-to-read display. Stop/start and reset controls are included for all three

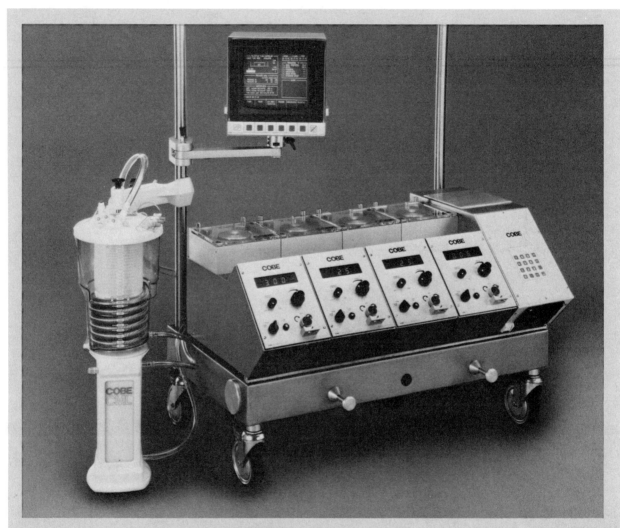

Computerized perfusion controller (courtesy of Cobe Laboratories)

timers. The computerized perfusion controller is just one of several electronically controlled devices that are used in hospitals and medical clinics.

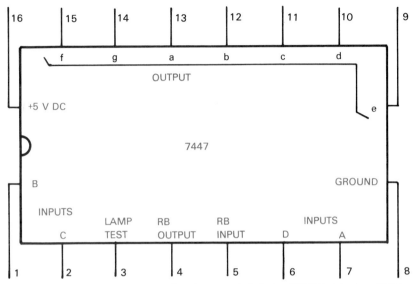

**Figure 10-18.** Pin-out diagram of a binary coded decimal (BCD) detector-driver

## DECODERS

Of course data that is encoded into a computer must also be decoded in some way to make it easy to use. A good example of a simple *decoding* circuit is the 7447 IC. The IC is called a decoder-driver, and it is used to decode the binary numbers 0000 to 1001 into the decimal numbers 0 to 9, Figure 10–18.

## LIGHT EMITTING DIODES (LED)

The 7447 IC decodes by driving (causing to light) the correct combinations of *light emitting diodes* (LEDs) that make up a *seven-segment display* or readout. (A seven-segment display is a group of LEDs set up in a pattern.) Figure 10–19 shows a seven-segment display of LEDs. Many watches and calculators use LED displays.

An LED, like an ordinary diode, is a semiconductor made in such a way that it allows electricity to flow in one direction through it but stops it when it tries to flow in the opposite direction. When the electricity flows through it, an ordinary diode gives off energy as heat, but an LED gives off energy as light. Differing colors of light are produced by varying the materials within the LED. Figure 10–20 shows how a decoder-driver decodes a number and displays the results on a seven-segment display of LEDs.

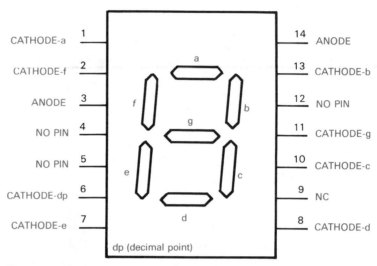

**Figure 10-19.** Pin-out diagram of a seven-segment LED digital display

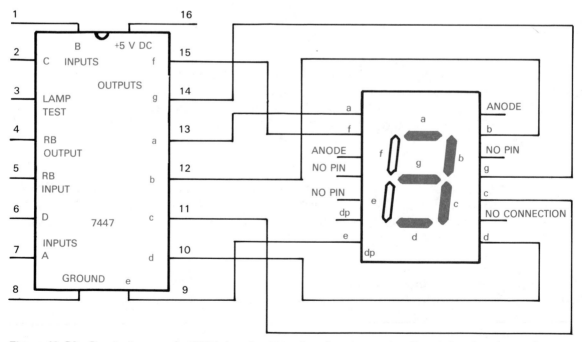

**Figure 10-20.** Circuit diagram of a 7447 decoder-driver decoding the number 3 and showing the results on a seven-segment display

Although seven-segment LED displays are useful for many patterns, they cannot produce diagonal lines. A more convenient form that can produce diagonals is a *dot-matrix display.* It involves making electrical connections to selected columns and rows to light specific LEDs to form numbers, letters, or other symbols.

Figure 10–21 shows five columns and seven rows of LEDs. By applying the proper voltage to row A and column 3, the LED at that location will light as indicated in Figure 10–22. In actual practice, the proper voltage would be applied in turn to rows A through G in rapid order. Also, if only the third column continued to receive the proper voltage, a solid pattern would appear as shown in Figure 10–23. This pattern would represent the number 1. Since the dot-matrix display can show letters as well as numbers, it is sometimes called an *alphanumeric display.*

*Liquid crystal displays* (LCD) are used on watches, small calculators, and on some hand-held video games because they require much less power than LEDs. Since they use less power, smaller batteries can operate them. Batteries of standard size may be used but they will last longer than those used to light LEDs. For complex digital devices, a video monitor similar to a television receiver is used to display data.

**DOT-MATRIX DISPLAY**

**LIQUID CRYSTAL DISPLAY (LCD)**

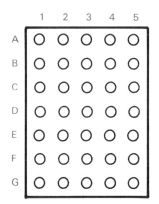

**Figure 10-21.** Dot-matrix display

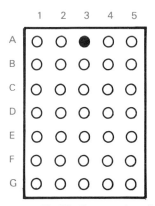

**Figure 10-22.** Dot-matrix display with one lighted LED

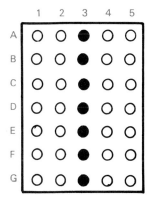

**Figure 10-23.** Dot-matrix display showing the number 1

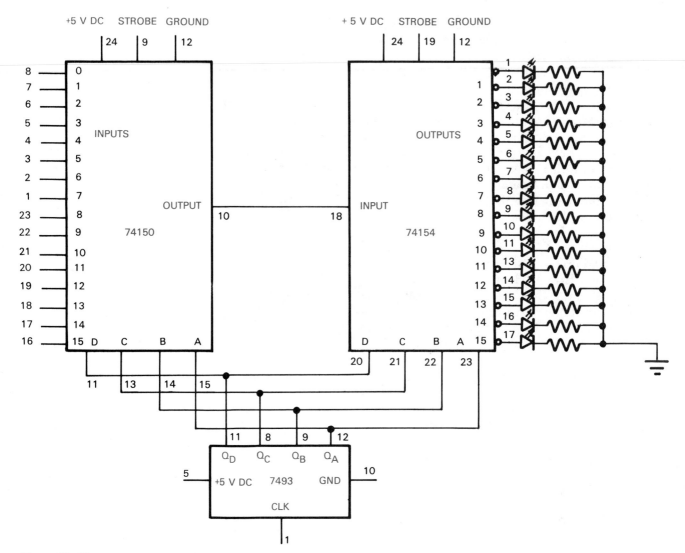

**Figure 10-24**

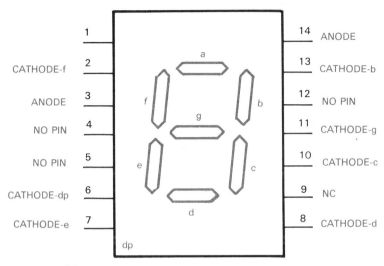

**Figure 10–25**

**SUMMARY**

The binary number system, although ideally suited for electronic circuitry, is sometimes inconvenient for people to use. To make binary numbers less difficult to use, codes such as the BCD and Gray code have been developed.

Data in digital form can be transferred from one location to another by encoding it at the transmitting end and decoding it at the receiving end. To make digital data easy to read and understand, displays that show numbers and letters are used. Types of displays include the light emitting diode (LED), dot matrix, and liquid crystal (LCD).

## REVIEW QUESTIONS

1. Convert the following binary numbers into BCD: 10011, 11001, 01111.
2. Convert the following decimal numbers into BCD: 35, 48, 101.
3. Convert the following numbers from Gray code into decimal: 1001, 1010, 11111. Use Figure 10–5 to help you.
4. In the Gray code, how many digits must be changed from the number 7 to the number 8?
5. How is the data from input 7 selected to be transferred to the output of the 74150 IC?
6. Explain how, with only one data input, the 74154 can allow for sixteen different outputs.

7. Which LEDs or segments would be on to show the number 3 on a seven-segment LED display? See Figure 10–18.
8. What is an advantage of a liquid crystal display (LCD) over an LED display?

## SUGGESTED ACTIVITIES

1. Build an encoder-decoder circuit. Follow the schematic shown in Figure 10–24.
2. Experiment with LEDs by lighting the individual segments. Follow the diagram shown in Figure 10–25.

# 11

## MEMORY CIRCUITS

After studying this chapter, you will be able to:
- Program data into a memory circuit.
- Recall data from a memory circuit.
- List the differences between RAM and ROM memories.
- Give the advantages of PROM or EPROM memory ICs over a ROM memory IC.
- Describe several hardware types of memory devices.

## OVERVIEW

The memory circuits and devices you will learn about in this chapter are designed to store data in digital form either temporarily or more or less permanently. Memories can be either volatile, which means they lose what is stored in them when the power goes off, or involatile, which means they keep the data stored in them when the power goes off.

**RAM**     *RAM (random access memory)* circuits are usually made in an integrated circuit. One simple RAM IC—the 7489—can be used as an example of how RAMs work.

Chapters 7 and 8 discussed the process of storing information in the form of binary 1s and 0s. The flip-flops discussed in Chapter 7 are also used in the 7489 IC. The flip-flops are arranged so that a 1 or 0 could be put in and/or taken out of any one of them without disturbing or going through the other flip-flops. Because of this arrangement, they are called random access memories (RAMs).

The 7489 is made up of sixteen different rows called *words* in which data can be stored. Each word is four bits long. A total of sixty-four bits of data can be stored in the 7489. Figure 11–1 shows the layout of a 7489 RAM IC. In order to use or change any of the data, you must select the exact word and bit you want to use or change. The process of selecting is called *addressing* and is similar to putting the street and house number on a letter.

In the 7489 there are four select-address inputs which allow you to choose any of the sixteen words by entering a binary number. For example, to select the "word" 5, make the proper connections to pins 1, 15, 14, and 13, as shown in Figure 11–2. To input the data—for example, the number 1001—in word 5, make the necessary connections to pins 4, 6, 10, and 12.

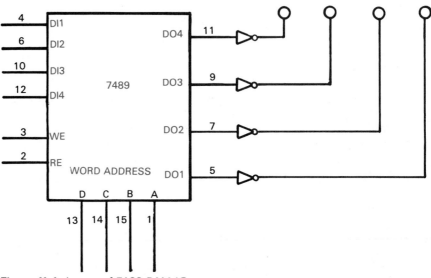

**Figure 11-1.** Layout of 7489 RAM IC

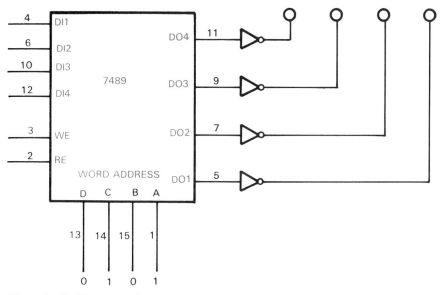

**Figure 11-2.** Diagram of 7489 RAM IC when the word 5 has been selected to enter data

Figure 11-3 shows the data ready to be placed in the memory location of word 5. Next, to put the binary number 1001 into memory, momentarily connect the write enable pin 3 to a 0. (The process of entering data into memory is called *writing* or the write operation.) Only when pin 3 is at 0 will data be placed into memory. Figure 11-4 is a table showing the placement of the binary number 1001 into word location 5 of the 7489 IC.

In order to recall or use the data stored in memory, a process called *read* is used. By setting the select-address inputs to the word location 5 and also setting the *read enable* pin 2 to 0, the data is displayed by the output in binary form, as shown in Figure 11-3. Notice that the output pins 5, 7, 9, and 11 are connected to inverters. The inverters put the data back into the same form in which it was entered.

There are much more complex memory ICs available. They may have more than four bits per word; eight, sixteen, and even thirty-two bits are common. They may also have hundreds or thousands of word locations and be able to store vast amounts of data.

In discussions or advertisements about computers, you may have heard people say that a particular computer has 64K or 128K or 256K memory. They are referring to the approximate number of bytes that a particular computer memory can handle. (A *byte* is eight bits, and a *bit* is a 1

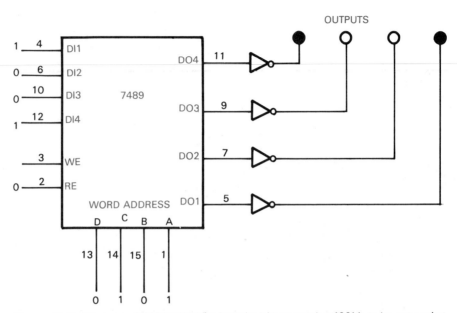

**Figure 11-3.** Diagram of 7489 RAM IC when the binary number 1001 is to be entered at word 5 and displayed at the outputs

or a 0. K is an abbreviation for kilo, which means one thousand. Therefore, 64K is equal to 64,000 bytes.) The actual number of bytes can be found by successively doubling numbers starting with the number 2. Two doubles to 4, 4 doubles to 8, 8 doubles to 16, etc., finally reaching 256, 512, and 1024. There are 1024 bytes in 1K. Therefore, 64K bytes is actually $64 \times 1024$ or 65,536 bytes. It would be time-consuming to address every word in a 64K byte memory manually. However, computers work very rapidly, and addressing all of the words in a 64K byte memory takes only a short time.

## ROM

ROM (*read only memory*) is different from RAM in two ways. Once a ROM is programmed, usually at the factory, the data it contains cannot be changed. However, the data can be read from it in much the same way that data is read from a RAM.

Another difference between ROMs and RAMs is that when a ROM is programmed, it keeps that data even though the power is turned off. ROMs are made up of physical devices like diodes or resistance fuses rather than flip-flops. (*Diodes* are electronic devices that allow electricity to flow in only one direction.) The diodes are placed so that they connect rows to columns, as shown in Figure 11-5. In this figure, current would flow from

| ADDRESS | DI4 | DI3 | DI2 | DI1 |
|---|---|---|---|---|
| WORD 0 | | | | |
| WORD 1 | | | | |
| WORD 2 | | | | |
| WORD 3 | | | | |
| WORD 4 | | | | |
| WORD 5 | 1 | 0 | 0 | 1 |
| WORD 6 | | | | |
| WORD 7 | | | | |
| WORD 8 | | | | |
| WORD 9 | | | | |
| WORD 10 | | | | |
| WORD 11 | | | | |
| WORD 12 | | | | |
| WORD 13 | | | | |
| WORD 14 | | | | |
| WORD 15 | | | | |

**Figure 11-4.** Table showing data entered into word 5

column 1 to row A as long as the diode was intact. This current flow could equal a 0 in digital logic because there is little resistance in a forward-conducting diode, and very little voltage is needed to push current through it (low voltage drop). If the diode between row A and column 1 were removed, current could not flow. The resistance would be infinite, and the voltage drop would be equal to the source voltage or a digital 1.

When manufacturing ROMs, it is easier and cheaper to put diodes between all rows and columns and then burn out with excess voltage those diodes where a 1 should be stored in memory. This process of burning out the diodes programs the ROM. Since the diodes cannot be replaced, the program cannot be changed. This characteristic limits the use of ROMs to situations where the same data or instructions are needed over and over again. One such situation might be in a calculator that converts inches to centimeters. The conversion chart is stored in a ROM, and the data is used as needed.

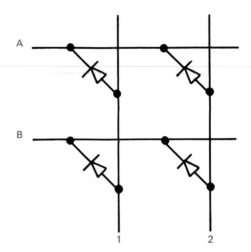

**Figure 11-5.** ROM memory using diodes

Another important use for ROMs is in microcomputers. Certain instructions that a microcomputer needs each time it is turned on are supplied by a ROM. (You will learn about some of these instructions in Chapter 13.) The process of setting up a ROM IC to contain certain data is expensive. Therefore, such ROMs are manufactured in large quantities to keep the costs low.

**PROM**        In some cases the user of ROM ICs would like the data the IC contains to be unique. In this case a *PROM* (programmable read only memory) could be purchased, and the user could program in the desired data. The IC is programmed by using a connecting material that is easily burned out, leaving a gap in the connection. (Nichrome wire has high resistance and a low melting point. It acts much like a fuse when excess current flows through it, Figure 11-6.) This type of ROM (programmable) cannot be changed once it is programmed.

**EPROM**        To solve the problem of not being able to change the data in a ROM once it is programmed, the eraseable programmable ROM was invented. An ultraviolet light is used to change the conduction characteristics of the silicon material used to make EPROMs. A transparent window on the top of

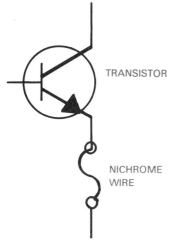

**Figure 11-6.** Diagram of a PROM. The nichrome wire has a low melting point and leaves an open circuit.

the IC allows the ultraviolet light to be focused on the IC chip to change the data contained in it. EPROMs are used in video game circuits to allow for occasional changes in the games.

## STORAGE AND RETRIEVAL

Microcomputers need a great deal of external memory storage for storing programs. Two popular means of providing easily accessible but also relatively permanent external storage for microcomputers are magnetic tape and magnetic discs. The magnetic tapes and discs are made of plastic with a layer of ferromagnetic material. When the tape passes a coil such as a recording head, its particles take on a magnetic polarity. Data can be stored by simply assigning a north polarity (1 in digital) and south polarity (0 in digital), as shown in Figure 11-7. More complex methods of storing data or magnetic materials are usually used to keep the number of errors (incorrect data) to a minimum.

To retrieve data from the magnetic material, the tape or disc passes by a coil of wire, and the moving magnetic field induces a voltage in the wire. The polarity of the voltage depends upon the polarity of the magnetic field. The induced voltage is amplified and shaped into a digital pulse for a microcomputer to use.

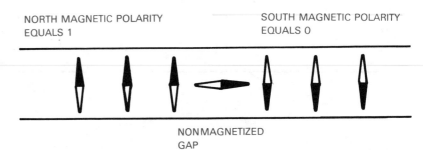

**Figure 11-7.** Data recorded on magnetic recording tape

Another method for storing data on a magnetic material is to store tones or frequencies. One frequency can be used to represent a 0, and a different frequency to represent a 1, Figure 11–8.

It is less expensive to use magnetic tape for storing data than to use magnetic discs. Many common brands of audio tape recorders can be used with some types of microcomputers, but other microcomputer manufacturers design a special tape recorder which is the only type of recorder their microcomputer will use.

Magnetic tape has all of the data placed in order from one end to the other. To retrieve data that is located in the middle of the tape, you must either run the tape fast forward or reverse it to the desired spot, which sometimes is a slow process.

Magnetic discs have data recorded in bands or tracks around the disc, as shown in Figure 11–9. Discs can be randomly accessed. In other words, data can be entered or retrieved from any of the tracks without going through the other tracks.

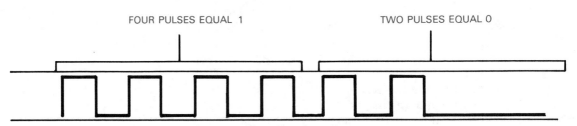

**Figure 11-8.** Magnetic tape using varying frequencies to record data

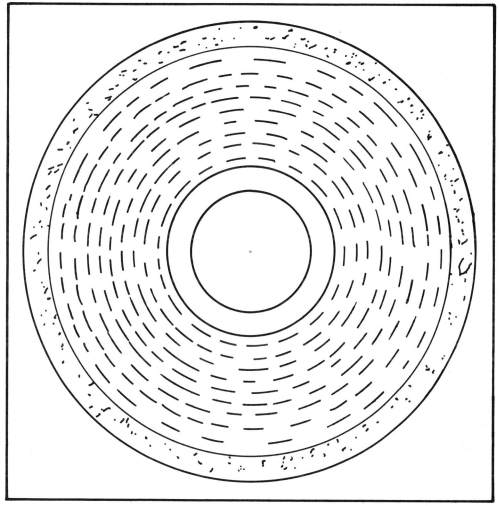

**Figure 11-9.** Floppy disc with data recorded in randomly accessible bands

Discs can be accessed much faster than tapes so computer programs can be loaded much more quickly from discs. Random access of data on a disc is an even bigger advantage that discs have over tapes. Random access allows the computer to get data from a disc when it is needed to run a program rather than to have to load it all in the computer before the program is run, as is the case with most tape storage units.

One popular disc used with microcomputers is made of a thin plastic material and is only 5 1/4 inches in diameter. Because it is made of a thin plastic and is quite flexible, and because it is smaller than the 8-inch discs that were commonly used, it is called a *mini floppy disc*. Computers commonly use two mini floppy disc drives. A program can be stored on one disc and data filed on the other disc.

To protect the mini floppy disc from damage, it is housed in a thin plastic pocket in which it is free to move. The recording play heads have access to the disc through a slot cut in the jacket. Figure 11–10 shows the various parts of a mini floppy disc.

Larger and more sophisticated tapes and discs are used with large computers.

## Laser Storage

A method other than magnetic means of storing data is by the use of a laser. Data in digital form is stored on a disc as microscopic (so small it can only be viewed through a microscope) pits etched into a reflective foil. The laser beam is focused on the foil, and as the disc rotates, the beam is interrupted by the pits and is reflected back to a photodetector that converts the laser energy into electrical impulses.

## *Microprocessor Engine Control*

The microprocessor shown is so powerful it can process a million commands a second. At 55 miles an hour this computer can read seven engine parameters and change seven engine functions in less than an engine revolution—three hundredths of a second. The computations performed during each minute of engine operation would take a human being using a manually operated calculator an estimated 45 years or more.

All of these computations are performed with chips (ICs). One is a custom high-performance microprocessor; the other is a large-capacity memory chip. The microprocessor is so precise that under any engine operating conditions it can make the proper adjustments in fuel-air

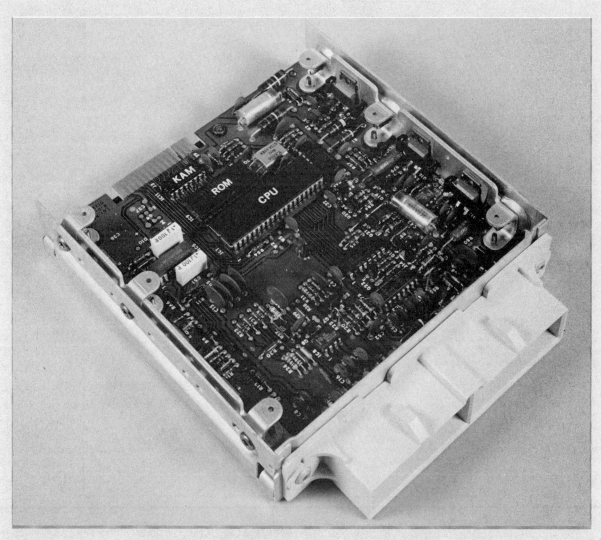

This microprocessor can process a million commands a second (courtesy of Ford Motor Company).

mixture, making it leaner or richer as needed. It can also adjust the spark timing, advancing or retarding it to meet the current conditions. These adjustments and others allow the engine to run nearly perfectly no matter what the conditions or how rapidly they change.

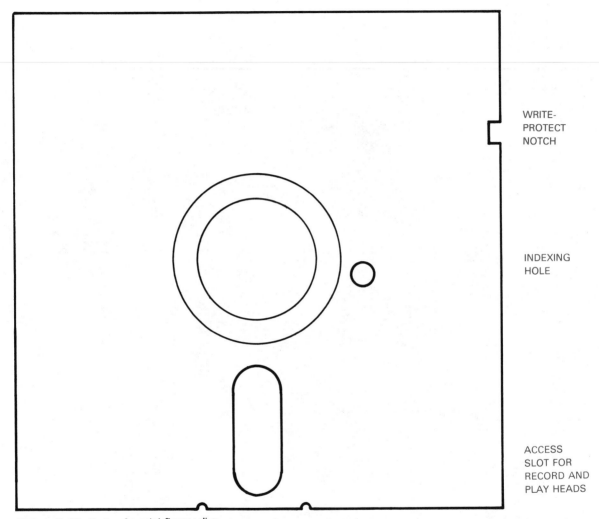

WRITE-
PROTECT
NOTCH

INDEXING
HOLE

ACCESS
SLOT FOR
RECORD AND
PLAY HEADS

**Figure 11-10.** Parts of a mini floppy disc

**SUMMARY**      In this chapter you learned that some types of microcomputer memory storage devices such as the RAM lose their memory when power is turned off while others such as ROMs do not. You also learned that you can only read data from ROM memories and that that data cannot be changed once the ROM is programmed. PROMs, however, can be programmed to individual user needs, and EPROMs can be reprogrammed as necessary.

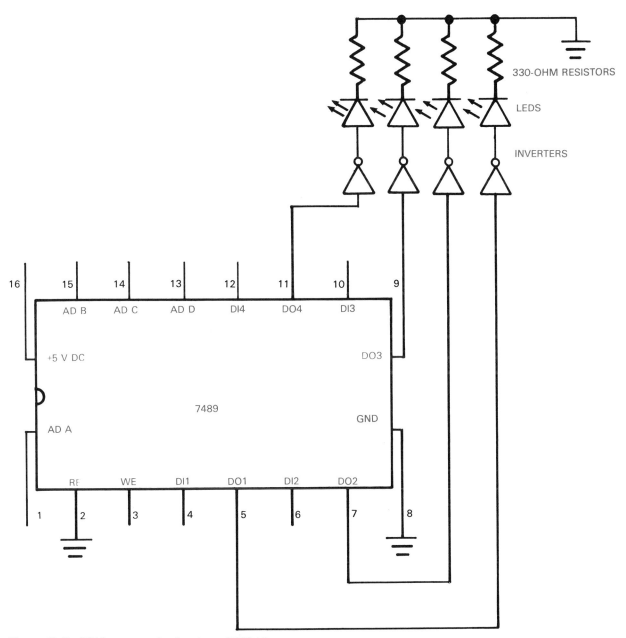

**Figure 11-11.** RAM memory circuit using a 7489 IC

In addition, you learned that microcomputers need external memory storage and that magnetic tape and discs are common methods of storing data for microcomputers to use.

## REVIEW QUESTIONS

1. List a disadvantage of a RAM when compared to a ROM.
2. How many four-bit words are contained in a 7489 RAM IC?
3. How many bits of data can be stored in a 7489 RAM IC?
4. Give an advantage of using a PROM rather than a ROM in a computer device.
5. What is the difference between a PROM and an EPROM?
6. A 1K byte memory is actually how many bytes of memory?
7. What is an advantage of using magnetic tapes over using floppy discs for computer data storage?
8. What is a disadvantage of using a magnetic tape when compared to using a floppy disc?

## SUGGESTED ACTIVITIES

1. Using a 7489 memory chip, build the circuit shown in Figure 11-11.
2. Store the number 1989 in memory using the following steps:
   (1) Connect all select addresses—pins 1, 13, 14, and 15 to a 0 (low). These connections select memory address location 0000 in the 7489 IC.
   (2) To write the one from the number 1989 in the preceding memory location, connect pin 4 (data 1 input) to a 1 (high). Connect the other data inputs, pins 6, 10, and 12 to a 0 (low). These connections allow the binary number 0001 to be entered.
   (3) Momentarily connect pin 3 (write enable) to a 0. This step enters or writes the preceding number into memory.
   (4) Be sure that pin 3 is not connected to a 0. Connect select address A (pin 1) to a 1. Leave the other select addresses connected to 0. You will be able to write data into memory address location 0001.
   (5) To enter the number 9 from the number 1989 into memory, connect the data inputs in the following manner: Connect pins 4 and 12 to a 1 and pins 6 and 10 to a 0. The binary number 1001 is now ready to be written into memory.
   (6) Repeat step 3.

(7) Be sure that pin 3 is not connected to a 0. Connect select address B (pin 15) to a 1 and the other select addresses to 0. The circuit is now set up to write data in memory address location 0010.

(8) The number 8 from the number 1989 can now be entered into memory by connecting the data inputs as follows: Connect pin 12 to a 1 and pins 4, 6, and 10 to 0s. The binary number 1000 will be written into memory when you complete the next step.

(9) Repeat step 3.

(10) Be sure that pin 3 is not connected to a 0. Connect select addresses A (pin 1) and B (pin 15) to 1s. Leave the other select addresses at 0. The memory address location 0011 can now have data written into it.

(11) To enter the second 9 from the number 1989 into memory, repeat step 5.

(12) Repeat step 3.

(13) Be sure that pin 3 is not connected to a 0. To read the data that was entered into memory, set the select address pins to the address location 0000. (Refer to step 3 if necessary.) If pin 2 is not already connected to a 0, be sure to connect pin 2 (read enable) to a 0. Record as a decimal number the number stored at this location.

(14) Change the connections to the select address pins so that memory location 0001 is addressed. (Check step 4.) Record the number to the right of the number in step 13.

(15) Change the connections to the select address pins so that the memory location 0010 is addressed. See step 7. Record the number to the right of the number in step 14.

(16) Finally, change the connections to the select address pins so that memory location 0011 is addressed (refer to step 10). Record the number to the right of the number in step 15.

(17) The number that you have recorded should be 1989—the same number that you entered into memory.

(18) Carefully put away all components and equipment that you used in this experiment.

# 12

# DIGITAL TO ANALOG AND ANALOG TO DIGITAL CONVERSION

## OBJECTIVES

After studying this chapter, you will be able to:
- List several examples of the use of digital to analog and analog to digital converters.
- Convert digital data to analog form.
- Convert analog information to binary code for use by digital circuits.

## OVERVIEW

So far in this book you have learned about digital electronic circuits that are controlled by digital-type inputs whose outputs control other digital-type circuits or digital readouts. However, it is often useful to be able to control an analog device with outputs from digital circuits or to provide inputs to digital circuits from an analog source.

*Analog circuits* do not have two set values like 0 and 5 volts as digital circuits do, but instead vary continuously over a range from low to high or high to low, as shown by the graph of the AC voltage in Figure 12-1. So that analog circuits can control digital circuits and digital circuits can control analog circuits, special circuits called D to A (digital to analog) and A to D (analog to digital) are used. They are called D/A and A/D converters. Just as an interpreter allows two people who speak different languages to communicate with each other, the D/A and A/D converters allow digital and analog circuits to communicate or to interact with each other.

The digital readouts that you are familiar with which have an analog source might be a temperature gauge, a voltmeter, the speedometer in your car, etc.

Analog devices that are operated by digital circuits may not be as obvious, but they include devices such as blenders and microwave ovens, where you set the speed or temperature by entering the data through a keyboard. Robots are also a good example of digital circuits controlling analog devices. The motors that propel the robot or that cause parts of it to move, such as the motors to its arms, are controlled by the robot's digital computer circuits.

In simple terms a D/A converter takes binary numbers or combinations of binary numbers and changes them into corresponding voltage values. For example, a binary output of 1 can equal 1 volt, a binary 2 equals 2 volts, a binary 3 equals 3 volts, etc., Figure 12-2. As you may remember

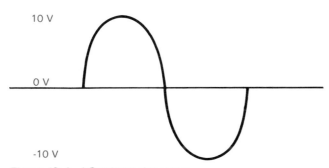

**Figure 12-1.** AC voltage sine wave

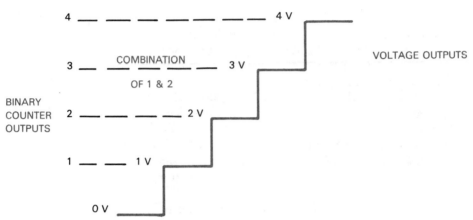

**Figure 12-2.** Binary counter outputs converted to analog voltage

from Chapter 1, voltage (measured in volts) is the electrical pressure that pushes the electrons. The greater the voltage, the more the electrons move. This movement of electrons is called current flow and is measured in amps.

### Resistor-Ladder Network

There are several ways to convert digital to analog. One method is called the *resistor-ladder network.* It works by dividing the voltage output of 5 volts (high or 1 output of digital logic circuits) into smaller amounts, using a component called a resistor. Resistors are difficult for electrons to get through. The higher the resistance the fewer electrons that can get through. In Figure 12-3 you can see that resistor R1, which has a resistance value of 100,000 ohms (resistance values are measured in ohms), allows only half as much current to flow as R2, the 50,000-ohm resistor.

If another resistor, R3, were added to the circuit in Figure 12-3 and its value were half of R2, or 25,000 ohms, then current flow through it would be twice as much as the current flow through R2 and four times greater than the current flow through R1, Figure 12-4. Current flow through these resistors corresponds to binary number place values of 1 to 2 to 4, etc. In Figure 12-5 if the binary number 001 was present, R1 would allow a small current to flow.

### Summing Amplifier

An amplifier circuit called a *summing amplifier* can convert a small current flow to an amplified voltage at its output, Figure 12-6. If the binary number changed to 010 as in Figure 12-7, R2 would allow twice as much

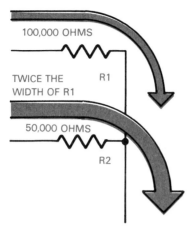

**Figure 12-3.** Current flow in two unequal value resistors

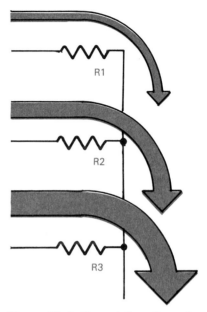

**Figure 12-4.** Current flow through three unequal value resistors

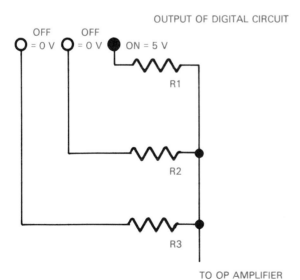

**Figure 12-5.** Resistor ladder with 5 volts appled to R1

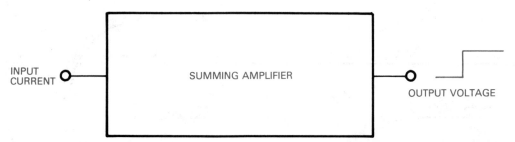

**Figure 12-6.** *Output voltage of summing amplifier with 001 binary input*

current to flow to the summing amplifier as was the case in Figure 12-6. The output of voltage through the summing amplifier would double, as shown in Figure 12-8.

If the binary number changed again, this time to 011, current would flow through both R1 and R2, which would be added together going into the summing amplifier and would cause the output voltage to be as shown in Figure 12-9. Notice that the voltage actually increases in small steps rather than gradually.

The circuit in Figure 12-9 works quite well for converting small binary numbers into an analog voltage. However, as you can see, the larger the binary number, the higher the current flow. This is true because not only do the resistors get smaller as the binary number gets larger, but there are also more paths for current to flow through.

## The R 2R Ladder

To avoid the problem of too much current flow, another circuit for D to A conversion can be used. This circuit is the *R 2R ladder*. It divides the

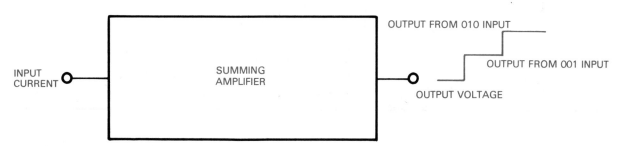

**Figure 12-7.** *Output voltage of summing amplifier with 010 binary input*

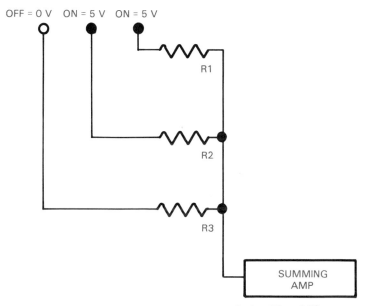

OUTPUT OF DIGITAL CIRCUIT

OFF = 0 V    ON = 5 V    ON = 5 V

R1

R2

R3

SUMMING
AMP

**Figure 12-8.** Resistor ladder with 5 volts applied to R1 and R2

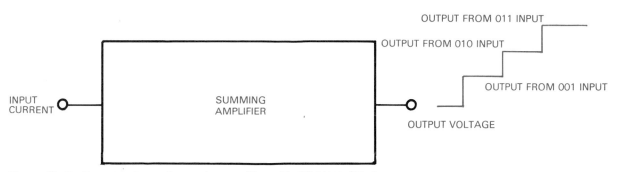

INPUT
CURRENT

SUMMING
AMPLIFIER

OUTPUT FROM 011 INPUT

OUTPUT FROM 010 INPUT

OUTPUT FROM 001 INPUT

OUTPUT VOLTAGE

**Figure 12-9.** Output voltage of summing amplifier with 011 binary input

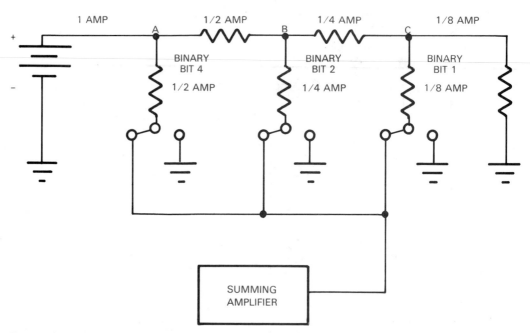

**Figure 12–10.** R 2R network showing current dividing at each junction

total current flow into parts according to the value of the binary number. In an R 2R ladder circuit that has circuit paths with the binary place values 4, 2, and 1 available, current would flow only in the place value 4 path if the number 4 were being converted from analog to digital, Figure 12–10. When the binary number 2 is converted from digital to analog, only one-fourth of the total current available in the circuit flows to the summing amplifier. This is one-half the amount of current flowing when the number 4 was being converted from digital to analog. If the binary number 1 is converted from digital to binary, only one-eighth of the total current flows. This is one-half the current flow of when binary 2 is being converted.

    To convert from digital to analog any binary numbers other than 1, 2, 4, 8, etc., combinations of these numbers are used. For example, binary number 3 is a combination of binary 2 and binary 1. The current flow to the summing amplifier is the two separate currents added together—in this case, one-fourth of the total plus one-eighth of the total. This adds up to three-eighths of the total current flow available. In this electrical circuit the current divides up because of the values of the resistor. Each amount of current is then converted to a corresponding amount of voltage by a summing amplifier.

To understand the circuit in Figure 12-10, follow through the example of the water distribution system in Figure 12-11. A water pipe of a certain diameter is connected to a Y that divides the water into two equal halves. At junction B in Figure 12-12, pipe 2 is divided by a Y into equal halves. Each half will contain one-fourth of the original water flow in pipe 1. At junction C in Figure 12-13, pipe 4 is divided into two equal pipes, each allowing one-eighth of the volume of water in the original pipe to flow. Finally, if at junction D in Figure 12-14 pipe 6 is split into two equal parts, the volume of water in each would be one-sixteenth of the original amount in pipe 1.

Now, if a valve were placed just in front of each of the junctions and each valve were controlled by a place value of 8, 4, 2, and 1, as shown in Figure 12-15, then water flow through pipes 3, 5, 7, and 9 would have a volume proportionally in size that corresponds to the binary place values of 8, 4, 2, and 1.

With a little understanding of R 2R circuit series and parallel circuits, you can understand how the current divides proportionally for each bit, just as the water was divided in the water distribution system described. Only two values of resistors are needed for the circuit. One value is just double the other value. (To make it easy to compute the resistances and thus easier

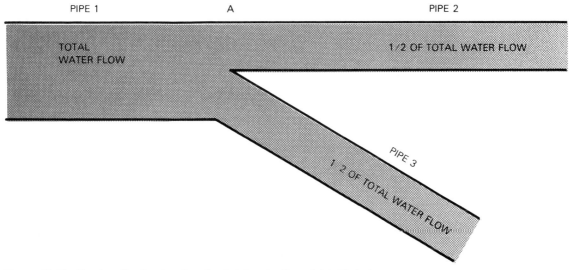

**Figure 12-11.** One junction in pipe showing total water flow divided in halves

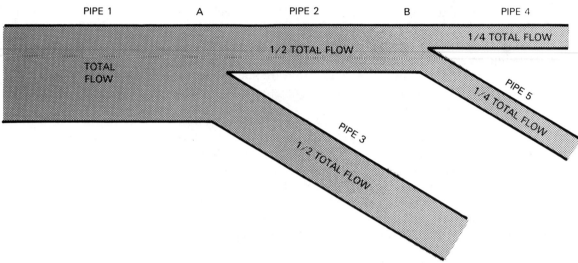

**Figure 12-12.** Two junctions in pipe showing how flow is divided

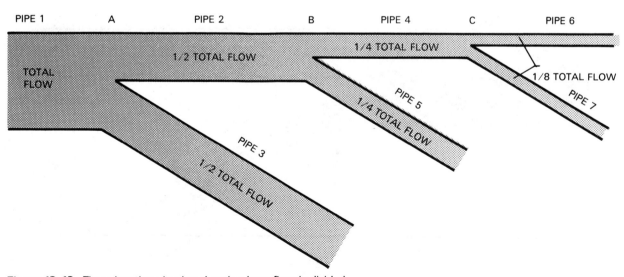

**Figure 12-13.** Three junctions in pipe showing how flow is divided

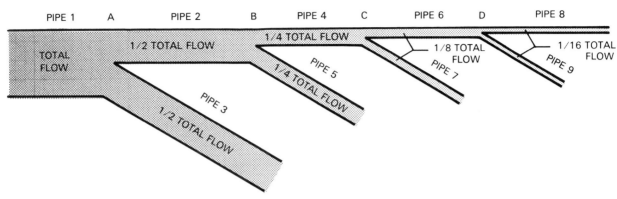

**Figure 12-14.** Four junctions in pipe showing how flow is divided

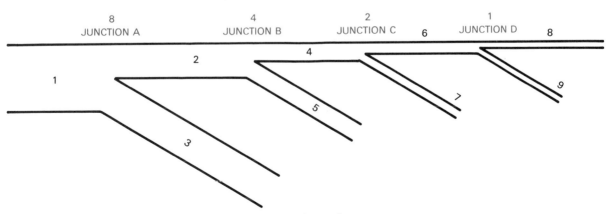

**Figure 12-15.** Comparison of junctions in pipe to binary place values

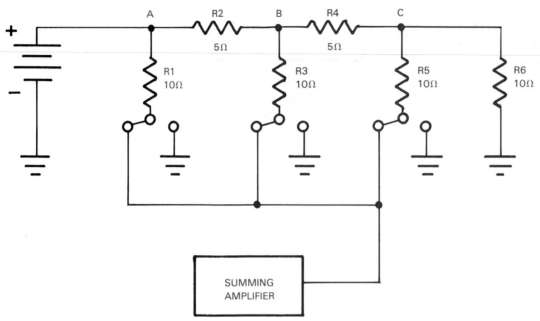

**Figure 12-16.** Resistors in R 2R network

to understand the circuit, the value of the resistors in the example will be 5 ohms and 10 ohms. These small values would not be used in an actual circuit.)

In the circuit in Figure 12–16, where the current divides at each of the Ys or junctions in the circuit, either path or branch that it takes has the same resistance and the current divides in equal amounts. One-half of the current available at that junction goes each way at point A in Figure 12–16. The current divides through R1, which equals 10 $\Omega$ and through the combination circuit of R2, R3, R4, R5, and R6 which also has an equivalent resistance of 10 $\Omega$. To prove that the combination equals 10 $\Omega$, use a parallel-circuit formula. First, find the resistance of R5 and R6 in parallel by applying the parallel-resistance formula:

$$R \text{ equivalent} = \frac{R5 \times R6}{R5 + R6} \quad RE = 5.$$

Next add R4 = 5 $\Omega$ to the RE = 5 $\Omega$ because they are in series with each other. (In a series circuit the total resistance is the sum of the individual resistors.) The total resistance of RE + R4 = 10 $\Omega$. This is in parallel with R3, which is

10 Ω. Therefore, the parallel-circuit resistance formula is again applied to give a new equivalent resistance of 5 Ω. As you can see, the resistance in each branch circuit from point A to ground is 10 Ω. This causes the current to divide in half, as shown in Figure 12–17.

At point B in Figure 12–18, the two branches again have the same resistance to ground. (This can be proven by using the same formulas applied earlier.) The current I, which is half of the total current flow, is divided into two equal parts, I3 and I4, at point B. I3 and I4 are each equal to one-fourth of the total current flow. Finally, at point C, the current again divides because of equal resistance through each branch into I5 and I6. I5 and I6 are equivalent to one-eighth of the total current flow. It should be noted that changing SW1, SW2, or SW3 from the ground connection to the summing amplifier connection does not change the resistance of the circuit.

The operation of the summing amplifier will not be explained in detail in this text, but it consists of an operational amplifier (called an OP amp) and resistors that control the amount of gain of the amplifier. The output of the OP amp is limited by the power supply voltage applied to it.

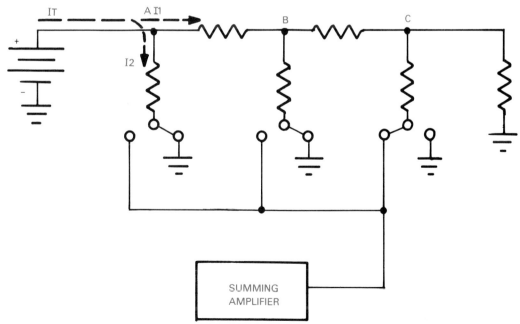

**Figure 12–17.** Current dividing in half at junction A

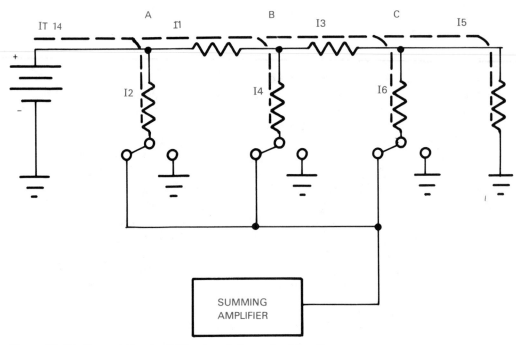

**Figure 12-18.** Current flow in R 2R network through all junctions

**D/A CONVERTER IN AN IC**     As with many electronic circuits, most of the circuitry that is used in a D/A converter can be built into a single IC. There are many D/A converter ICs. One of them is shown in Figure 12-19. This IC is built into an 18 PIN DIP. It contains a resistor network and switches (semiconductor type) that, although different and much smaller, operate much like the discrete components described earlier in this chapter. As you can see in the functional diagram, the IC has eight digital inputs. That means, for example, that it can divide the output voltage into 255 steps, not counting 0 volts. When all of the inputs are 0, the output voltage is at its maximum. This condition is the reverse of the way the circuits described earlier operated. At binary numbers 127 and 128, the voltage is approximately one-half the maximum voltage. Finally, at 11111111, the output voltage is at 0. A change of one number in binary makes a change of 39.06 mV or .03906 volt. The voltage is output directly from the output amp. Power supply voltage, output range selection, etc., make up the other connections to this IC.

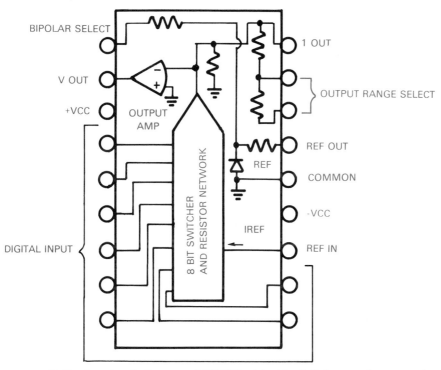

**Figure 12-19.** Functional diagram of DAC82 eight-bit digital to analog converter (courtesy of Burr-Brown Corporation)

Analog to digital conversion is probably used even more than digital to analog, but since the A/D converter explained in this text makes use of a D/A converter, the D/A was explained first.

A/D conversion is commonly used for meters that read volts, amps, etc., whose readout is made up of seven-segment displays. It is also used for automobile gauges like temperature, odometer, speedometer, etc. Another exciting use of A/D conversion is for the reproduction of music and video. Laser discs have digital bits of information stored on them that are picked up by the laser when the discs are played. One advantage of using digital methods of storing audio and video information is that the sound or picture can be enhanced (changed to more realistic level) by changing the binary number that represents certain tones or portions of pictures. For example, if

**ANALOG TO DIGITAL CONVERTER**

a tone created by a particular binary number was less than needed to sound realistic, that binary number could be made greater before the permanent recording was made.

A/D conversion also helps with computer-assisted drafting. Points on a drawing can be digitized (their X, Y axis values stored as binary numbers in memory). When the drawing is again needed on the monitor screen or a copy from the plotter is needed, these digitized points are used to reconstruct the drawing.

A/D converters make use of digital circuits you have already learned about, but the type of A/D converter to be explained in this text uses an analog-type circuit you may not be familiar with. This circuit is called a comparator. It compares two voltages and produces a voltage level equivalent to a binary 1 when one voltage is greater than the other. When it produces a voltage level equivalent to a binary 0, the voltage that was the greater is now less than the other.

## Comparator

The comparator makes use of an OP amp with two inputs, labeled A and B as shown in Figure 12–20. The OP amp is supposed to have a gain similar to the ratio of the voltage at input A to voltage at input B. However, since the output voltage cannot be any higher than the power supply voltage used, the output generally is about 3.5 V to 4 V, which is high enough to be used as a digital 1. To get the output voltage to be equivalent to

## *Computer-Aided Design and Drafting*

The operator of a CAD system works either from a keyboard or from the tablet menu. The tablet menu contains the most often used figures and shapes. To select an item from the menu, a cursor is placed over the item and a button is pressed. On a screen, menus are often used to allow the operator to select items without typing them on the keyboard. CAD systems can make a tremendous increase in the productivity of a draftsperson.

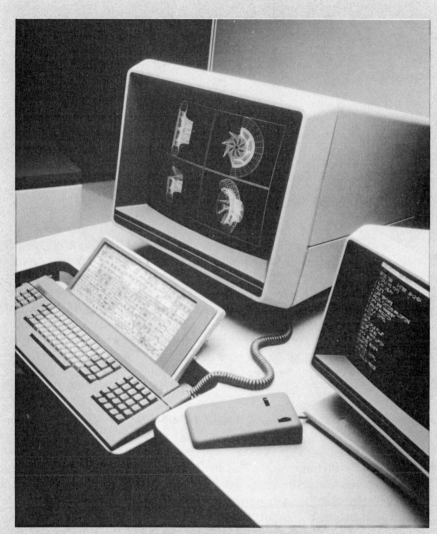

A computer-aided design system (courtesy of Auto-trol Technology)

Although CAD has been in use for several years, it had been limited to companies that could afford large main frame computers. CAD software is now available for microprocessors at an affordable price, so almost any company or school can afford it.

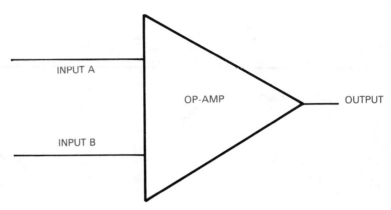

**Figure 12-20.** OP-amp symbol

a digital 1, input A must be larger than input B. If input B is larger than input A, the output voltage produced is a negative voltage. Since the type of logic gates described in this example operate on positive voltage, negative voltage simply acts like a 0 when applied to a logic gate. Therefore in a comparator, if the voltage at A is greater than the voltage at B, the output is a 1. But if the voltage at B is greater than the voltage at A, the output is 0.

Figure 12-21 is a block diagram of one type of A/D converter. Refer to it as necessary when reading the following explanation of an A/D converter.

## Example of Analog to Digital Conversion

The analog data that is to be converted to a digital value is connected to input A of the comparator. The analog data is in the form of a voltage, and, in this case, assume that it is a greater voltage than the voltage at input B. (If the counter is reset to 0, the output of the D/A converter is 0 volts, which makes the input at B 0 volts.)

If input A is 2.8 volts, then it is greater than input B. The output of the comparator is a 1, which is connected to one of the inputs of the AND gate. When the other input of the AND gate is also high because of a clock pulse, the clock pulse is passed through the AND gate to the counter. The clock pulse causes the counter to advance from 000 to 001. If each binary number value is .5 volt greater than the number before it, the output voltage of the D/A converter is now .5 volt. Since .5 volt is still less than 2.8 volts, the comparator still makes the input of the AND gate a 1, enabling the next clock pulse to pass through the AND gate and advance the counter. The

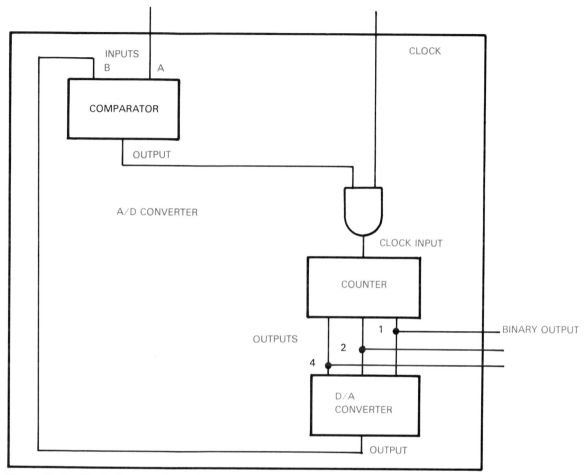

**Figure 12-21.** Block diagram of an A/D converter

output of the D/A converter advances to 1 volt, but that is also less than 2.8 volts, and the clock pulses continue to advance the counter as shown in Figure 12–22. When the counter reaches number 110, the output voltage from the D/A converter is 3 volts. Finally, the voltage at input B is greater than the 2.8 volts at input A of the comparator. This condition causes the output of the comparator to go to 0.

Now the input of the AND gate that is connected to the output of the comparator is at 0, and the AND gate can no longer pass the clock pulse through to the D/A converter. The output of the counter has stopped at the

| BINARY COUNTER OUTPUT | VOLTAGE TO COMPARATOR |
|---|---|
| 000 = | 0.0 V |
| 001 = | 0.5 V |
| 010 = | 1.0 V |
| 011 = | 1.5 V |
| 100 = | 2.0 V |
| 101 = | 2.5 V |
| 110 = | 3.0 V |

**Figure 12-22.** Voltage levels produced by D/A converter in an A/D converter

number 110. The 2.8 volts analog was converted to the binary number 110. The time it took the counter to count from 000 to 110 was only a fraction of a second. The only number you can read at the output of the counter is 110.

This circuit was kept quite simple so that it would be easier to understand. In actual practice, a similar but more complex circuit would be used to allow smaller changes in an analog voltage to be changed accurately into corresponding binary numbers. The type of A/D converter described here is sometimes referred to as the successive-approximation type because with each increase in the binary number from the counter, the circuit checks to see if voltage B is greater than voltage A.

As with the D/A converter, many ICs are manufactured that contain the entire circuitry necessary to make an A/D converter. The pin-out diagram of a twelve-bit A/D converter appears in Figure 12–23. This particular A/D converter has twelve outputs arranged in order from LSB to MSB. There is also a not MSB ($\overline{\text{MSB}}$) to be used when the complement of a number is needed. This IC also has available two input voltage ranges— 10 V and 20 V; it is one of the successive-approximation A/D converters.

## SUMMARY

D/A and A/D converters are very useful because they allow analog devices such as motors to be controlled by digital circuits and digital devices like a digital automobile speedometer to operate from analog data. D/A converters consist of some type of dividing network, like a resistor ladder or an R 2R network. They also contain an OP amp that acts as a summing amplifier for the different levels of inputs it receives. A/D converters are often of the successive-approximation type, which means that a binary counter increases the output voltage of a D/A converter with each count until it just exceeds the voltage input to the A/D converter. At this point, the counter is stopped and its output is the binary value of the input voltage. Many ICs are made that can do A/D and D/A conversion.

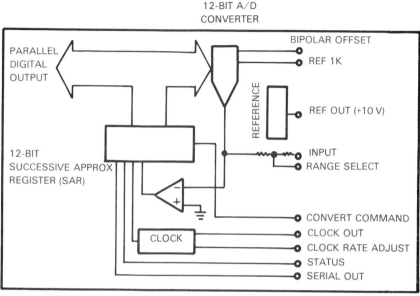

**Figure 12–23.** ADC10HT twelve-bit analog to digital converter (courtesy of Burr-Brown Corporation)

## REVIEW QUESTIONS

1. Explain the difference between a digital output and an analog output.
2. List and explain three examples where it is helpful to convert from digital to analog.
3. List and explain three examples of where it is helpful to convert from analog to digital.
4. What advantage does the R 2R method of dividing the electrical current into amounts that correspond to binary values have over the resistor-ladder network method?
5. What is the advantage of using 0 to 111 rather than 0 to 11 when converting from digital to analog?
6. Explain the function of the D/A converter in the A/D converter described in this chapter.
7. If a D/A converter contained in an IC had a six-bit input, how many steps would the output voltage be divided into, not counting 0 voltage as a step?
8. List three advantages of D/A and A/D converters that are built into an IC.

## SUGGESTED ACTIVITIES

1. Make a list of all the uses you have seen or heard about that use D/A converters.
2. Make a list of all the uses you have seen or heard about that use A/D converters.
3. Obtain an IC-type A/D and/or D/A converter. Following the spec sheets for them, do some experimenting. For example, use an oscilloscope to show the output voltage present from a D/A converter and use a seven-segment readout and a display decoder-driver to show the output of an A/D converter.

# 13

# THE DIGITAL COMPUTER

## OBJECTIVES

After studying this chapter, you will be able to:
- Name the main parts of a computer.
- Explain the basic concept of the central processing unit of a computer.
- List the basic steps that the microcomputer performs in the computing process.

## OVERVIEW

Computers use a combination of all of the digital circuits you have learned about such as counters, registers, encoders, decoders, adder/subtractors, clocks (clock pulses), etc. When most of these functions are performed by a single IC chip, this chip is called a microprocessor. When other IC chips are added to make a full-fledged computer, the computer is called a microcomputer.

## BASIC PARTS OF A COMPUTER

Figure 13–1 shows a block diagram of the main parts of a microcomputer—the input, the central processing unit, the memory, and the output. Devices like keyboards, joysticks, etc., are used as inputs to microcomputers. The *central processing unit (CPU)* includes the *arithmetic logic unit (ALU)*, registers, and buses to communicate with input, output, and memory. The memory of a computer includes RAM, ROM, and external permanent devices such as discs and tapes. The output of a computer can go to a printer, to a video screen, or to control other machines.

## OPERATION

Instructions to the computer are given through the keyboard in a particular order called a *program*. Programs may also be given to the computer through a data storage device such as a disc or tape. Any data that needs to be processed is also included in a program.

The microcomputer first decodes the instructions from the language they are in to *machine language* (explained later in the chapter). Then it goes through a routine to complete the instructions provided. It uses temporary storage areas (registers) that are in the microprocessor to manipulate the data in operations such as adding, subtracting, comparing, etc. The computer also gets information it needs from its memory and places new information into the memory when directed to do so.

As long as the power is on, the computer stores entire programs including instructions, input data, and output data in its memory according to instructions. (Output data is the result of manipulation of input data.) In order to retain the information when the power is off, the computer operator must instruct the computer to record the information on a disc or tape or to make a hard copy on paper.

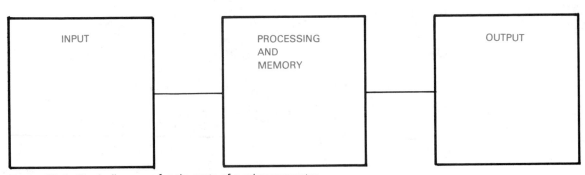

**Figure 13–1.** Block diagram of main parts of a microcomputer

The microcomputer makes the processed data usable by providing visual copy on a video screen, making hard copy from a printer, or operating some machine or electronic device according to instructions.

One of the ways to communicate with a microcomputer is through a keyboard. From the instructions given on the keyboard, the computer uses a process called encoding. Not only is each decimal number on a keyboard encoded into its corresponding binary number by the encoder, but each letter of the alphabet and even each character such as a comma(,), dollar sign ($), etc., are also encoded. The most commonly used system of encoding numbers and characters into binary numbers is the *American Standard Code for Information Interchange (ASCII)*.

## COMMUNICATING WITH A MICROCOMPUTER

### Assembly Language

Instructions to a microcomputer can be given in binary, but because binary numbers can be quite long and tedious to use, octal and hexadecimal numbers are used. Since remembering a particular number for each operation given to a microcomputer is difficult, a language of words that describe the operation the computer is to do has been devised. For example, you may wish to have the computer add, subtract, store, etc. The words used for instructions to the microcomputer are abbreviated to two- to four-letter words called *mnemonics*. The mnemonic word for subtract, for instance, could be sub. When mnemonics are used to give instructions to a microcomputer, the process is referred to as *assembly language* programming. Assembly language must be encoded to binary for the computer to understand.

### Machine Language

When instructions are given to the microcomputer with one of the number systems such as binary, the process is referred to as *machine language* programming. An example of how assembly language and machine language are used is the instruction "halt," which is used to stop the computer at the end of a program. The mnemonic for the word "halt" is "hlt." On some microcomputers the hexadecimal number for the term is 76$ ($ is the symbol for a string variable); the binary coded decimal number is 01110110.

There are many higher-level languages than assembly language for communicating with a microcomputer. Higher-level languages such as

Basic or Pascal use statements made up of more common terms and thus are easier for most people to use. A higher-level-language command may include several assembly-language instructions. Programs are written to translate these higher-level languages to assembly or machine language.

To get all of the instructions and data that are processed by a microcomputer from the input (keyboard, etc.) or memory to the central processing unit (CPU) and back to the memory or to an output device, a network of connections called *buses* are used. Buses may be 8, 12, 16, or more connectors in parallel with each other. Just as city buses carry people to and from the heart of the city, digital electronic buses carry electronic messages from the input or memory to the CPU and from the CPU to the memory or to an output device.

**CENTRAL PROCESSING UNIT**

The CPU is actually one or sometimes two or three IC chips which control all of the other parts of a microcomputer. All of the arithmetic functions, such as adding, subtracting, etc., and logic functions take place in the CPU. The CPU acts like a human brain. The brain gets its information from the senses and makes a decision. It then sends out signals to control actions. Similarly, a CPU gets information from an input or memory, processes it or makes a decision, and sends its results to an output to control signals.

If a person's hand touches something hot, a signal is sent to the brain. The brain interprets the message and decides, because of previous experience, that continuing to touch the object could be painful. It then sends out a control signal that causes the hand to quickly move away from the hot object. In an electric oven controlled by a microprocessor, a heat sensor sends a signal to the CPU. The signal has been changed electronically to a digital value. The CPU decides whether the temperature is too hot or too cool by comparing the signal value with a value that has been previously programmed into it. It then sends out a signal to cool or heat the oven as is necessary.

In a microprocessor the order in which all of the operations take place is controlled by a permanent program in the IC chip itself. This program is stored in ROM.

Figure 13-2 diagrams the various sections that make up the CPU. The next few paragraphs describe what each of these sections does, and an exercise that will show each section in action follows.

### Arithmetic Logic Unit

The *arithmetic logic unit (ALU)* is part of the CPU and performs the basic arithmetic functions, such as adding and subtracting. It also performs logic functions like those of AND, OR, inverter, and Exclusive OR gates.

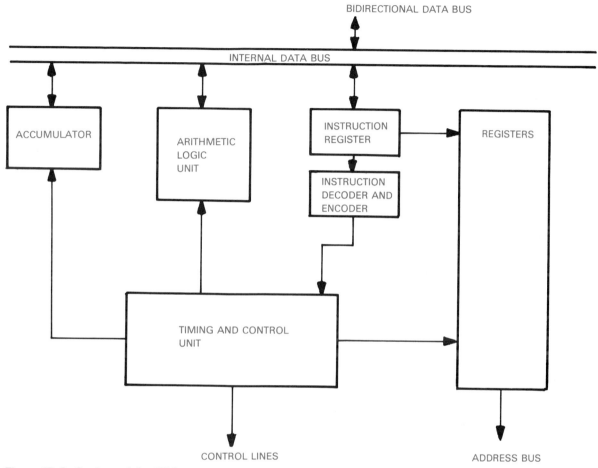

**Figure 13-2.** Sections of the CPU

The ALU can be used to solve incredibly complex problems. It is made up of full adder/subtractors and logic gates.

## Accumulator

The *accumulator* is a register like those you learned about in Chapter 8 and is used for temporary memory storage. The accumulator works very closely with the ALU. For example, if the microcomputer is to add two numbers together, one of them is usually placed in the accumulator, and,

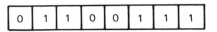

**Figure 13–3.** Eight-bit storage register

after the two numbers have been added, the sum is placed in the accumulator.

The accumulator also acts as a direct link or supply source for the output(s) of the microcomputer. In other words any data that is going to be output to a device such as a video screen or printer must first be placed in the accumulator and then output from there.

The accumulator is not the only register in the CPU. Several others are also needed to store instructions that are given to the microcomputer. When two numbers are added together, one number is placed in the accumulator and the other in one of the registers. These registers usually can store eight bits of information like the binary number shown in Figure 13–3. Frequently registers are put in pairs so that they can handle sixteen-bit or larger numbers as shown in Figure 13–4.

## Clock

A part of the CPU that may or may not be a separate chip or chips is the clock. As you learned in Chapter 7, a clock is simply a circuit that generates electrical pulses at regular intervals. The clock function in a CPU is very critical. It synchronizes (makes happen at the same time) certain events and allows others to occur only at particular times. For example, the clock does not allow inputs and outputs or data buses to work at the same time.

In the example of two numbers being added together by an adder/subtractor, one of the numbers is supplied by the accumulator, and one by another register. Because the numbers may arrive at different times, without synchronization there would be the possibility that the computing might start before all of the second number had arrived, and the sum might be incorrect. However, by not allowing the adder/subtractor to give an output until the clock pulse arrives, you can be certain that both numbers are present even though they arrived at different times. The clock is also used to synchronize some operations that the microprocessor must do over and over again in a particular order.

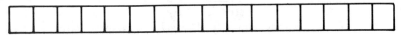

**Figure 13–4.** Sixteen-bit storage register

## Program Counter

The *program counter* also uses the pulses from the clock to function just as the counters in Chapter 9 do. Its job is to keep the instructions in the microcomputer in order.

**MEMORY**

The CPU of a microprocessor has a small amount of temporary memory, but it must have access to a large memory. In fact, the larger the memory it works with, the longer and more complex the programs that it can handle.

In Chapter 11 you learned about different kinds of memories and how they worked. Just as you addressed different memory locations mechanically, the CPU must be able to address them electronically to store information in memory. The instruction to "write" must be given to the microcomputer as well as the location at which it should be stored.

To retrieve or use information that is stored in memory, not only must the command "read" be given to the computer, but also the location of what you want read. Reading something from memory does not destroy it or remove it from that memory location. This type of memory is "built-in" memory that all microcomputers have to some extent. The amount of built-in memory is increasing with each new generation of computers.

**OUTPUT**

The last basic part of a microcomputer to be discussed is the output. A microcomputer may have more than one output device connected to it, in which case the program must contain the specific instructions as to how to output the data.

Most microcomputers use a *video monitor* that not only allows you to see on a screen what you have typed in from the keyboard (input device) but that also displays the processed data in a written or graphic form. Video monitors work like a TV set. (In fact, TV sets are many times used for monitors.) The difference between a monitor and a TV set is that a monitor does not contain the circuitry that allows a TV to pick up and process signals transmitted by television stations.

Printers are connected to microcomputers so that you can get a "hard copy" of your program or the data that has been processed. Printers use various methods for transferring the ink onto the paper, but they all must contain decoding circuits that decode the electronic signals into recognizable letters, characters, or shapes.

A microcomputer may also use its output to control electrical/mechanical devices such as microwave ovens, food processors, metal lathes, automobile engines, etc. The processed digital signals of a microcomputer may control the speed, direction of rotation, and length of time a motor runs. They may control temperature, fluid level, etc., of various devices.

## Compact Disc and Laser Disc Players

The development of the compact disc player was a major breakthrough in the playback of recorded music. Not only is the sound quality greatly improved but also the semiconductor laser and microprocessors now used are less expensive to produce, smaller in size, and much more reliable than the mechanical devices used to play records and tapes. These advantages of the CD player as compared to conventional stereo are just a part of the added features available with the CD player.

Digital readouts can indicate the length of a time a disc has been playing or the length of time left on the disc. Even more advantageous is the ability to program the music available on a compact disc to be played in any order—selections can be left out or repeated as desired.

Players that can play both audio compact discs and video laser discs are now available and have the obvious advantage of providing great music or movies with excellent video and sound qualities using only the one machine. Laser video discs now have digital audio sound tracks rather than analog sound tracks.

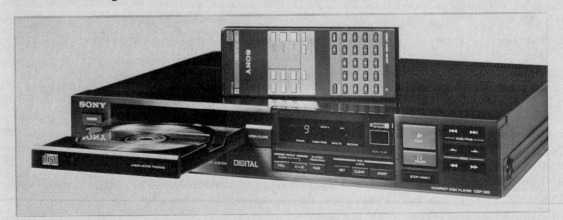

A compact disc player (courtesy of SONY Corporation of America)

When a microcomputer is first turned on, it goes through a process of *initialization* that clears the memory and prepares the computer to receive instruction. The initialization program gives instructions to put zeros in all memory locations and clears them much as one would clear a calculator before entering a problem. The initialization program is stored in ROM.

After the memory is cleared and the microcomputer is ready to receive instruction, a program may be loaded into the memory. To carry out a simple program such as monitoring an electric oven, the computer goes through steps similar to the following:

## INITIALIZATION AND OPERATION

1. The CPU starts by checking to see what instructions are in the memory. This process is called the *fetch* instruction. The first step in the program itself should contain an instruction rather than data because without an instruction, the CPU would not know what to do with the data. In general terms the first step of the program might read:

   "1. Load a register with the number designating the desired oven temperature, which is stored in a specific memory location."

   The CPU would then send out a "read" command along the control bus, address the specific memory location through the address bus, and bring the data into the specified register through the data bus.
2. The second step would be similar to the following:

   "2. Load accumulator with data from an input device."

   The CPU would select the input and send a signal through a control bus to enable (allow access to) that device. If more than one input were available to the microcomputer, the program would have to tell the computer which input device to enable. In order to give the proper instruction in the program, a number is assigned to each input device. In the case of the oven, the input would be from a heat sensor whose output would be converted to a digital signal and transferred through a data bus to the accumulator.
3. The third step requires the computer to subtract the contents of the register from the accumulator. This operation takes place in the ALU, and the results are left in the accumulator.
4. Finally, the contents of the accumulator are sent to a specific output device. The CPU sends out a signal to enable the proper output device, and the data is sent on a data bus to that output, which might be a video monitor, a printer, etc. This simple program would not have much advantage over making the readings manually, but it illustrates how the microcomputer functions.

**SUMMARY**    The description of how digital electronics circuits work together to make a computer was very general, but the basic concepts can be applied to help you understand the operation of specific computers. The CPU controls all of the functions of the microcomputer, but it must receive instructions in the proper order. Instructions are given through various input devices and in various computer languages. However, the CPU works from machine language, which is binary coding. There can be different output devices connected to the microcomputer, and just as input instructions are encoded to produce binary output, displays are decoded from binary to output the desired form. All of the operations of microcomputers are kept synchronized through the use of clock pulses.

## REVIEW QUESTIONS

1. Instructions provided in a specific order to a microcomputer are referred to as a _____.
2. Explain what is meant by the term "machine language."
3. Give an example of assembly language.
4. Explain why assembly language is easier to use than machine language.
5. What is the part of the CPU that keeps track of the steps of operation as they occur in a microprocessor?
6. What is the circuit that is contained in the CPU that does simple arithmetic problems?
7. What is the name given to the register that is always used for arithmetic problems and contains the answer once the problem is solved?
8. In the instruction to load data from memory into a register, what information other than the register and the data would need to be given?

## SUGGESTED ACTIVITIES

To learn some important facts about the personal computer that you may have in your home or one that you use in school, check the user's manual or call a computer store that handles that particular brand of computer. You could also ask a computer science teacher, an electronics teacher, or some other person knowledgeable in computers. Try to find the answer to the following questions:

1. How much memory does your computer have? (64K, 128K, 256K, etc.)
2. What type of microprocessor chip does your computer use? (8080A, Z80, 6502, etc.)

# 14

# PRACTICAL APPLICATIONS OF MICROPROCESSORS

## OBJECTIVES

After studying this chapter, you will be able to:
- List and describe several uses for digital electronics.
- List and describe uses of microprocessors in personal and business computers.

## OVERVIEW

In this chapter you will learn that there are many uses for digital electronics other than just computing or record keeping. Microprocessors are ideally suited to control any machines that have movement or to enhance the operation of any device that produces audio or video. Other digital electronics circuitry appears in hundreds of everyday devices.

## MICROPROCESSORS IN THE AUTOMOBILE

Microprocessors were first used as engine controls in automobiles in 1977. Since that time, their use has grown so that practically all new cars use some kind of microprocessor-based engine control. Two major factors that led to the use of microprocessor-controlled engines were the need for better fuel economy and the need to control automobile exhaust emissions. The problem of controlling spark timing (firing of a spark plug to ignite the air-fuel mixture in the cylinder at exactly the right time) was so complex that it could not be done with enough accuracy by using mechanical methods. Even though mechanical devices often work fairly well at a particular moment, they cannot change quickly enough to allow for changes in engine speed, load conditions, etc. However, microprocessors have the ability to act almost instantly upon the data that is fed into them and to provide an output to control the spark timing and air-fuel mixture over a wide range of operating conditions.

The microcomputer that controls the engine in an automobile is sometimes referred to as the on-board microprocessor. Data for the on-board microprocessor is gathered by seven to ten sensors that detect such things as temperature changes (both in the engine and in surrounding air), vacuum pressure, airflow, throttle position, acceleration rate, crankshaft location, etc., Figure 14–1. From all of the input data, the microprocessor makes adjustments in the ignition and fuel systems of the engine. It adjusts the fuel metering system, the air intake, the precise time that the spark plug fires, etc. All of these adjustments can be made in less than one engine revolution. If an engine were running at 3000 rpm, it is possible that it could be readjusted at least 3000 times in one minute.

The on-board microprocessor with additional memory capability records any malfunction of the computer-controlled functions of an engine. These malfunctions are sometimes stored in code form. Each malfunction is assigned a particular number, and they are output as a combination of flashes of a light on the dashboard. For example, a combination of one long flash and two short flashes may mean the number 12. If the number 12 were assigned to the airflow sensor, the mechanic would know that the airflow sensor was malfunctioning.

### Computer Control in Other Parts of the Automobile

Many other features within an automobile, such as temperature control and suspension system that uses electronically controlled air shocks, may also be controlled by a microprocessor—usually a different microprocessor from the one that controls the engine.

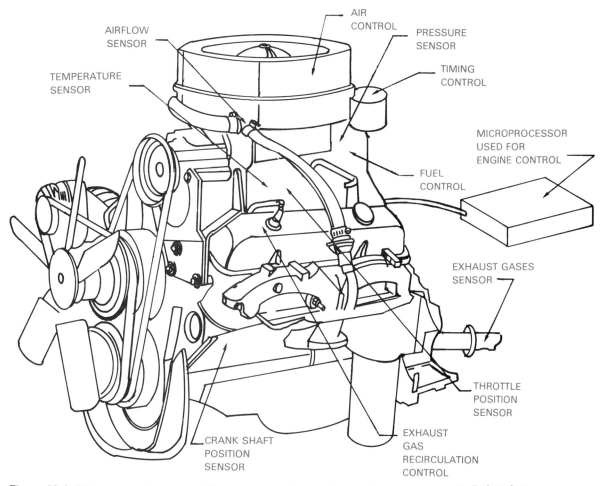

**Figure 14-1.** Diagram showing some of the sensors and controls on a microprocessor-controlled engine

## Digital Circuits in the Automobile

Automobiles contain many digital devices—digital clocks, digitally tuned radios, digital door locks, a voice warning system, digital gauges, and the speedometer. Digital door locks are a security as well as a convenience device, Figure 14-2. Not only does the owner not have to carry a key for the car door, but if someone who does not know the code tries to enter the car, an alarm sounds. Digital lock combinations are stored in a computer memory. By pushing the buttons of the lock in the proper sequence, the correct numbers are decoded. The logic circuit then has the output necessary to activate the circuitry that unlatches the lock. It also

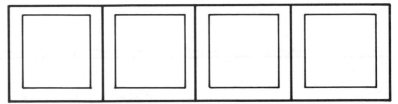

**Figure 14-2.** Combination lock with four push buttons. This lock could have many different combinations.

deactivates the alarm. If the buttons are pushed in the wrong order, the alarm circuitry is activated.

Voice warning systems simply use sensors to monitor logic circuits. When a problem occurs, these logic circuits control a voice synthesizer which tells you about the problem. For example, it may say "Your lights are on" if the ignition key is off but the lights are still on. Digitally tuned radios and compact discs are used to provide excellent quality sound systems in the automobile.

## Automotive Electronic System

The Ford Motor Company has developed an automotive electronic system that puts ten vehicle controls at the driver's fingertips and provides vast amounts of information at the touch of a cathode ray tube (CRT) screen in the instrument panel.

The system is called comtech. The five left-hand switches on the driver control pod activate the headlamps, the park lamps, the windshield wipers, the windshield wiper speed, and the windshield washer. Five right-hand switches control the radio (volume, seek, and memory), the windshield defroster, and a sequential scan of the CRT.

The CRT can also be controlled by a ten-button control panel located directly below the screen. By touching the keyboard buttons, the following data are flashed on the screen:

- Automatic temperature control functions with day/ date/clock
- Fuel economy information including graphs that indicate average fuel economy, instantaneous fuel economy, and miles to empty

- Trip information such as distance traveled, distance to destination, average speed, and estimated time of arrival
- Time functions including an alarm clock
- A monthly calendar that can be scanned forward or backward
- A mode control including speed alarm and service reminder
- Vehicle operating and service information
- Diagnostic checkout for various vehicle functions
- English to metric conversion
- A standby mode which blanks out the screen except for the word comtech

In the case of the climate-control screen, words like "hi," "auto," "lo," or "vent" appear on the screen. When touched, each word selects the system mode and makes an adjustment. Touching the word "warmer" raises the inside temperature while touching "cooler" reduces it.

The computer and wiring for the driver-control pod have multiplex control, dramatically reducing the number of wires required in the steering column. The system has a self-test capability.

Automotive electronic system (courtesy of Ford Motor Company)

## DIGITAL SOUND SYSTEMS

Digital sound systems are not only used in automobiles but also in homes and other places. Digitally encoded discs have greatly improved the quality of recorded music. Microscopic pits etched into a perfectly reflective foil that is laminated to the protective coating on a compact disc "store" the music. A laser beam is aimed at the foil that contains the pits, Figure 14-3. As these pits pass quickly over the laser beam, they break the beam up into impulses of light that are reflected onto a photodetector. The photodetector changes the light pulses into rapid on/off pulses (1s and 0s) of electricity. The pulses are very fast and transmit flawless audio signals to the amplifier.

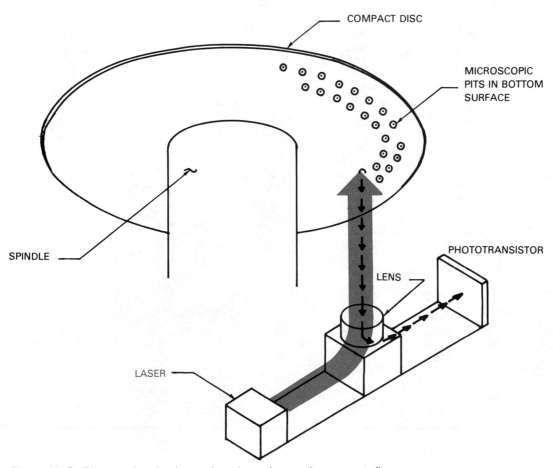

**Figure 14-3.** Diagram showing how a laser is used to read a compact disc

Unlike a record with a needle running in a groove, this sound system puts no wear on the disc. If any dirt or scratch causes a brief loss of digital information, decoding circuits can take replacement information from computer memories to fill these weak spots before the digital signal is changed into audio.

Microprocessors can select material on a disc in any order. This method of recording allows you to skip any part of the disc you wish and repeat other parts if desired. Digital readouts tell you exactly where you are on the disc at any time.

Microprocessors are also used in the R.F. (radio frequency) section of radios, Figure 14-4. Digital circuits set to decode exact radio frequencies are assigned to specific radio stations by the Federal Communications Commission (FCC). This permits you to select only the station you tune to and reject all others.

**DIGITAL TUNING**

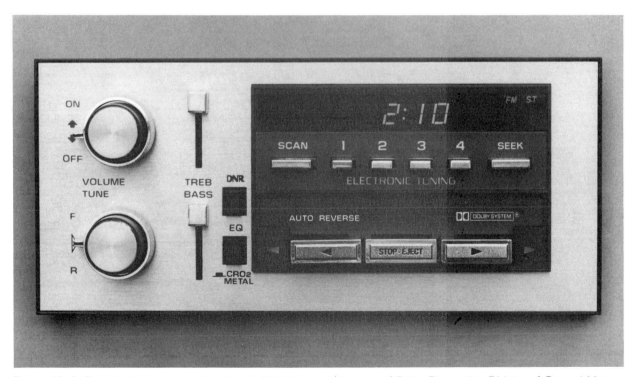

**Figure 14-4.** Bose music system receiver that is digitally tuned (courtesy of Delco Electronics, Division of General Motors Corporation)

Since controlling the tuning of a radio uses only a part of a micro-processor's capabilities, it is also used to provide other features. For example, if a small amount of power is constantly provided, the microprocessor can remember the station you were listening to when you shut off the radio, and it will go back to that station when you turn it on again. It can also be programmed to act as a complex clock radio. You can tune to one station until the radio shuts off at night, yet wake up to a different station in the morning. In fact, depending upon the amount of memory the microprocessor has, it can even turn your radio to different stations throughout the day so that you will not miss your favorite program.

## DIGITAL SYNTHESIZERS

Microprocessors not only allow you to listen to digitally stored and processed music but you can also use them to help you create your own music. Although synthesizers have been around for a long time, they used to be too large and too expensive for most individuals. The reason for their size and expense was that the sounds were created with bulky analog-type oscillators that took numerous electrical connections to function in coordination with each other. Storage of notes or chords had to be done on tape, which is slow and expensive. Miniature digital circuits replaced the oscillators. RAM and ROM memory chips replaced the tape memories and microprocessors coordinate all of these circuits to make present-day synthesizers much more versatile and capable, Figure 14–5.

These synthesizers range in capability from small portable but useful units to large sophisticated units that can accurately duplicate all of the sounds of a grand piano and invent new ones. In fact, a synthesizer can generate the sounds created by most musical instruments. The real advantage of synthesizers over musical instruments, however, is that even someone with limited experience can play harmonies along with the melodies that the synthesizer plays from preprogrammed memories.

For people who write music, there are printers that print out melodies, sharps, flats, rests, bar lines, stave lines, and accompaniment chord names. If changes need to made in one or more notes, those changes can simply be entered into the microprocessor and the memory will be updated. When the piece of music is played back from memory, the corrections or adjustments will have been included.

## DIGITAL TELEVISION

Not only has the creation and reproduction of audio been greatly improved by microprocessors, but video has also been affected. Microprocessor chips take the incoming broadcast signal and break it down into digital information, then reassemble the information for display on the

**Figure 14–5.** *Digital music synthesizer (courtesy of Casio Inc.)*

screen. The integrated circuits used in digital TVs are of the very-large-scale-integration (VLSI) type. One of these chips converts the incoming video signal from analog to digital before processing and then back to analog after processing to drive the electron guns in the picture tube.

Another chip processes the video and provides the microprocessor chip with measurements of the red, green, and blue signal levels. The microprocessor chip compares these signal levels with the preferences set by the user and modifies the values accordingly. One of the chips controls the deflection of the electron beam on the face of the screen. Digital control of this deflection gives more precise control which results in a sharper picture.

Audio is also processed digitally in monaural or stereo. Digital ICs provide a real advantage because one VLSI replaces hundreds of components that an analog TV requires and so the assembly process is much simpler. Also, using VLSIs makes it easy to automate production, which lowers assembly costs. The final alignment and testing which once was done manually can now be done with a microprocessor, which makes that process faster and more precise.

Another feature unique to digital sets is that the chips can be programmed to compensate for changes in the picture tube brought on by

**Figure 14-6.** Engineer at a computer-aided-design work station holding a microprocessor-based digital tuning system from a Zenith color television set (courtesy of Zenith Electronics Corporation)

aging. Digital sets have circuitry that senses the reflected signals which cause "ghosts," and additional circuitry can eliminate most of them. Because of these features, the picture produced by digital TV sets is sharper and purer than most analog sets.

Digital sets can display as an inset in the corner of the screen a small freeze-frame image from another channel. Memory chips store the information needed to display the freeze frame. Digital circuits in TV sets have become more common than analog circuits and have improved the picture quality, Figure 14–6.

The picture-tube control for a TV screen is also controlled by digital circuits, and monitors used with computers have improved graphics capability because they use digital ICs.

## GRAPHICS ON A CHIP

Complex software has been used to produce graphics on a computer screen, but hardware in the form of a digital IC can produce graphics more quickly. Combined with large-capacity memory chips, graphic chips can be used to produce bit-mapped graphics, which is similar to the dot-matrix display but on a much larger scale. There can be a million or more *pixels* (dots) on a screen, each having its own memory location. An image is created by addressing the necessary memory locations and providing a 1 to those you want lit and a 0 to those you want dark. Although this process produces graphics with superior resolution, there is still room for improvement. As the uses for better graphics increase, manufacturers will undoubtedly make ICs which provide them.

## COMPUTER-AIDED DESIGN

Computer graphics contributes significantly to computer-aided design (CAD). A CAD system appears in Figure 14–7. Microprocessor-based CAD systems are very capable and much less expensive than the early mainframe-based CAD systems. Most CAD systems have keyboards available for entering data, but other, easier-to-use devices like graphics tablets and digitizers with a mouse are also available. Other microprocessors use either a light pen or a touch-sensitive screen to enter data. The data entered as locations or points on the screen or graphics tablet are converted into digital data and stored in memory so that the image can be redrawn on the screen or plotted on paper to make a hard copy.

The advantages of the CAD system over conventional drawing are many. The designs can be stored in memory and then recalled to be changed or updated as needed. Often-used shapes are stored in memory to be called up as needed. Also, shapes can be enlarged on the screen, rotated for better views, and repeated as many times as necessary.

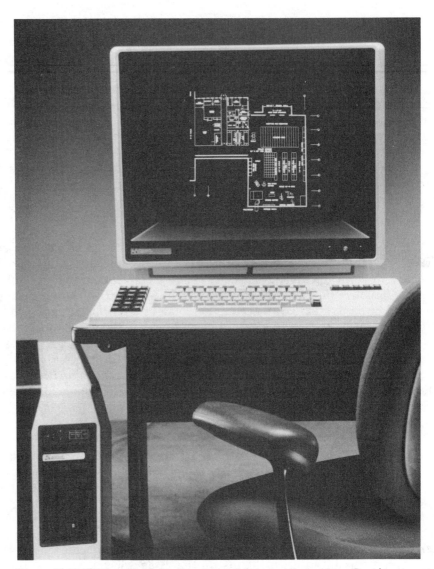

**Figure 14-7.** CAD work station (courtesy of Auto-trol Technology Corp.)

CAD systems save considerable time in making most drawings, but even greater savings can be made if the CAD system is able to generate instructions for computer-controlled manufacturing systems. This process is called CAD/CAM, computer-aided design/computer-aided manufacturing. A simple example of CAD/CAM is a drill press that bores holes in a part by receiving instructions as to the size and location of the holes from the computer on which the image was created.

## ROBOTS AND AUTO-MATED FACTORIES

The robot is another computer-controlled device used in manufacturing and other areas. Unlike computer-controlled milling machines and drill presses, which are stationary, robots can often move about, and have arms that can be extended and moved into several different positions. In fact, a more descriptive name than robot is "programmable manipulator."

The number of joints in a robot arm basically determines the complexity of the task a robot can perform. There are usually two ways to program a robot. The most common method is teaching by guiding. An operator uses controls to make the robot do the task required. As the robot goes through each step of the task, the computer is sensing and recording these movements in digital form. Once the task is completed, the computer can guide the robot through that task with little or no help from the operator. An example of this process is a robot that has a vacuum cleaner connected to it. The operator can direct the robot over the floor around the furniture while it is in the teaching mode. Then, by starting the robot in the very same spot each time the floor needs vacuuming, the computer will guide the robot through the task. When the furniture is rearranged, the robot will need to be taught the new pattern necessary to do the floor.

The other method of programming a robot is for the operator or programmer to write a program at a computer terminal. These operator-written programs can have extra features; for instance, if the robot is capable of sensing when a part is not present, it can skip a cycle or cycles and wait until the part is present.

The addition of more complex sensors is making dumb robots into not-so-dumb robots. One type of sensor resembling that on self-setting cameras uses a type of sonar to measure distance. Other sensors can measure pressure exerted by grippers on the robot arm so that the robot can pick up fragile objects without breaking them.

Robots are used in clean rooms (rooms where dust or contaminants cannot be present) to assemble electronic circuit boards and to inspect and measure newly manufactured parts.

Robots are useful in manufacturing plants. Some factories use a combination of automated machines that cut, drill, and machine parts and robots that transport these parts from one automated machine to another and load them into the machine for processing, Figure 14-8. Along with automated machines, robots can make parts and some finished products that are almost untouched by human hands. Some manufacturing plants can operate for periods of time with only a supervisor in a control room. However, this type of plant still takes people with a knowledge of electronics to design, control, and maintain them.

**Figure 14-8.** Overall view of the Kearney and Trecker flexible manufacturing system installed at Hughes Aircraft Company, Electro-optical and Data Systems Group (courtesy of Kearney and Trecker Corporation)

The number of applications for computers and the ease in using them has been increased by the development of devices that can recognize, analyze, and interpret visual images. Devices that can actually read and interpret pages of text use a process called *optical character recognition (OCR)*. The OCR process works by first converting images into binary numbers, then comparing the numbers to numbers stored in memory that represent characters (numbers, letters, and symbols) and interpreting those characters it recognizes to the user. One of the more common OCRs does not read pages of text, but it does read the bar codes on packages in supermarkets. OCRs also read the typewritten zip codes on pieces of mail and sort them accordingly.

## OPTICAL CHARACTER RECOGNITION (OCR)

Objects can also be identified by magnetic codes. These codes can be temporary (easily demagnetized) or permanent. The magnetic strip on plastic credit cards is an example of a code that can be converted to a binary number with use of a magnetic sensor.

Another coding system used for identification is called *passive integrated transponder*. It is a silicon chip about 1/16 of an inch square that is preprogrammed with a digital code. This chip is covered with a plastic sealant and attached or actually embedded in the item to be identified; it is activated only when an electromagnetic signal is passed over it. This system is used to identify dairy cattle, railroad cars and locomotives, and many other items where fast, reliable identification is needed.

Fast, reliable mail service has been a goal of the Postal Service since the days of the Pony Express. Now that goal has finally been realized. Electronic mailing is done by changing letter characters and numbers to a digital code and transmitting them over the telephone lines to their destination. At the receiving end, the digital code is changed back into its original form. This process takes only a few seconds, but it allows for much better communication between individuals and companies.

Other important uses for digital circuits and microprocessors are in the medical field. Almost all of the monitoring equipment used in hospitals has a digital readout, and much of the equipment contains a microprocessor that detects and records changes in conditions. In some cases an alarm sounds when conditions reach a danger level. Microprocessors are ideally suited for monitoring because of their high reliability and their ability to work precisely. Figure 14-9 shows medical equipment that has digital readouts.

Microprocessors are even used to help you take better photographs. The shutter speed and lens opening settings can be made automatically by some cameras. The film speed and amount of available light are fed into the

## DIGITAL CODING

**Figure 14-9.** Computerized perfusion controller (courtesy of Cobe Laboratories Inc.)

microprocessor, and it sends the signal necessary to adjust the camera for the correct settings. Figure 14-10 shows the microprocessor in a camera.

**SUMMARY**          This chapter mentions many uses for microprocessors. Some are uses you probably already know, but others may be unfamiliar. There are many other ways that microprocessors will be used in the future. You should be aware that the cars you drive, the stereos you listen to, the TVs you watch use microprocessors. They help create music, bring you radio broadcasts, make drawings, and design and manufacture equipment. You also learned that robots are computer-controlled devices with many industrial and home uses.

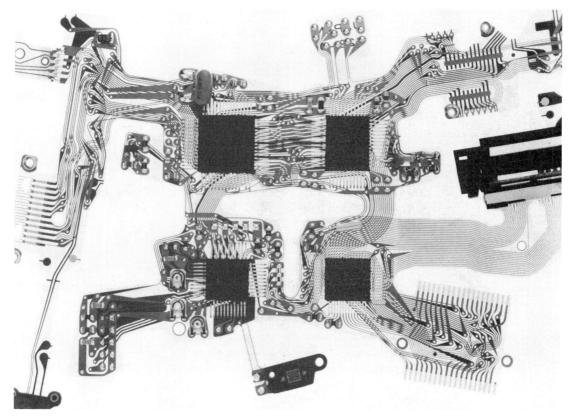

**Figure 14-10.** *Flexible printed circuit containing the main CPU and other ICs (courtesy of Minolta Corporation)*

You should know that digital codes can be used to identify objects, give pricing information, and even provide a means of fast, reliable mail. Also, without digital electronics, some of the medical equipment today would not function as well or may not even be available. Finally, you learned that even something as small as a camera can have a built-in microprocessor to help you take pictures.

## REVIEW QUESTIONS

1. List two major factors that led to the use of microprocessors for engine controls in an automobile.
2. Explain why microprocessors are so much better in controlling spark timing and air-fuel mixture than mechanical methods used previously.

3. List six conditions that are monitored by the sensor connected to the microprocessor of an automobile.
4. List three adjustments that the microprocessor makes in the ignition and fuel systems of an automobile.
5. Explain how music is stored in digital form on a compact disc.
6. What are two advantages of a compact disc over a record album for storing music?
7. How can the on-board microprocessor be used to aid a mechanic in repairing a car that is not operating properly?
8. Explain why synthesizers using microprocessors and digital circuits are so much better than synthesizers that use analog circuits.
9. Based on the number of components (mostly transistors) available on a digital IC, what type of IC is used in a digital TV?
10. Explain how digital TVs are able to produce a fine-quality picture even though a small part of the information needed to create the picture is lost in transmission.
11. How is the alignment and testing of a digital TV done?
12. What important change has been made to improve graphics on a computer monitor?
13. Explain the process of producing a simple graphic image on a monitor screen using bit-mapped graphics.
14. What do the letters CAD mean?
15. Explain why CAD is faster and better for producing a drawing than conventional drafting.
16. What do the letters CAM mean?
17. Another name for robot is _____.
18. Explain two ways in which robots can be programmed.
19. List three uses for a robot.
20. Robots sometimes replace people in jobs but they can also create jobs. Explain one new type of job robots could create.
21. Explain how OCR (optical character recognition) works.
22. What method other than visual can microcomputers use to recognize objects?
23. Explain how a passive integrated transponder can identify an object.
24. Explain how electronic mailing is done.

## SUGGESTED ACTIVITIES

1. Bring a newspaper or magazine article about some new use of microprocessors to school and share it with your class.
2. If possible, find a business or industry in your locality that uses robots and either arrange a tour through it or have someone from that company come to your class to talk about their robots.

# 15

# PROJECTS

After studying this chapter, you will be able to:
- Identify symbols of common electronic components.
- Read an electronic schematic so that you can build an electronic project from a schematic.
- List the steps in making a good solder joint.
- Lay out a pattern for a printed circuit from a schematic of a simple circuit.
- Mount components on a printed circuit board so that their values are readable and their pin alignment is correct.

## OVERVIEW

This chapter will provide you with experience in the actual building of an electronic device. Electronic projects of many different types may be built from preassembled kits, but some devices are not available in kit form or are less expensive when built from scratch. If you do not wish to use a kit, you may start with a schematic of the project you want to make, purchase all of the components and hardware, and make your own printed circuit board (PCB). A printed circuit board is a thin sheet of plastic or fiberglass that has a very thin layer of copper deposited on it, Figure 15–1. All of the copper except what is needed to make the electrical connections between components is etched away. Projects built from scratch will be discussed in this chapter.

## READING A SCHEMATIC

A *schematic diagram* uses symbols to show how components are connected together in a circuit. In a way it is like a road map that shows how cities are linked together with highways. From previous chapters in this book, you probably noticed that when the lines showing connections between circuits crossed, it did not mean that they were connected unless a dot was placed at the intersection. Illustrations in other publications may show that when wires cross, they are electrically connected *unless* there is a small loop in one of the wires where it crosses the other wire. Different methods of showing connections or nonconnections appear in Figure 15-2.

Another symbol used on schematics is the ground symbol. When one connection of a component is connected to the negative side of a power source, the ground symbol is shown rather than the connection, Figure 15-3. This symbol saves drawing some lines and makes the schematic less confusing because there are not so many lines crossing each other. In some instances the electrical ground (negative) connection is made through a metal chassis and is separate or isolated from the earth ground; the symbol used to indicate the chassis ground appears in Figure 15-4.

An IC may be represented on a schematic in two ways. One method shows the entire IC in a rectangular block with pins placed where they can be easily connected to the desired points. Figure 15-5 shows an IC with pins

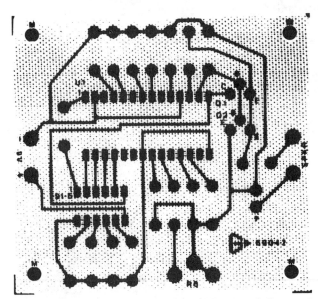

**Figure 15-1.** Printed circuit board (courtesy of Graymark International Inc.)

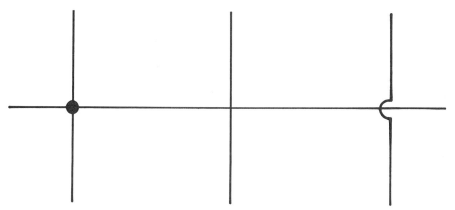

**Figure 15-2.** Reading schematics. The symbol on the left indicates a connection, and the symbol in the center indicates a nonconnection for drawings in this text. In other materials the symbol in the center indicates a connection and the symbol on the right shows a nonconnection.

**Figure 15-3.** Ground symbol used when connection is made back to the negative side of the power supply

**Figure 15-4.** Chassis ground symbol

arranged in other than numerical order for ease of use. The other method of showing an IC is to break it down into its various parts. For example, an IC that contains four AND gates may show separate AND symbols on the schematic, with appropriate pin numbers on them. Figure 15-6 shows such an IC. The power source connections may be shown on one of the symbols or on two symbols. Both methods are shown in Figure 15-7.

Most other common components have fairly universal symbols. Figure 15-8 is a chart showing the symbol and a pictorial for many common

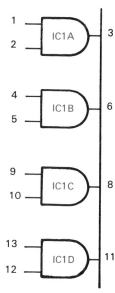

**Figure 15-6.** Parts of an IC represented schematically

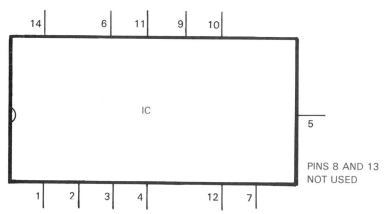

**Figure 15-5.** IC with pins out of order to make it easier to draw the schematic

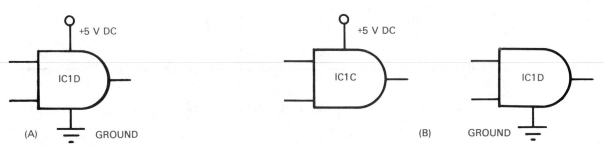

**Figure 15-7.** Methods of showing power connections to an IC

components. Symbols other than components that may be used on a schematic are shown in Figure 15-9.

There are two ways commonly used to give the values of components on a schematic. One way is to print the value or part number near the component, as shown in Figure 15-10. Sometimes there is not enough room on the schematic to print component values, and values are given on a separate parts list, Figure 15-11.

## PRINTED CIRCUIT BOARDS

*Printed circuit boards (PCB)* are used for most electronic devices because they are more reliable and take less space than point-to-point wiring. Also, circuits on a PCB are easier to trace. PCBs are usually made of a fiberglass or phenolic plastic base material, with a thin layer of copper deposited on it. PCBs hold components firmly and provide solid conduction paths between components.

## MAKING PRINTED CIRCUIT BOARDS

There are several ways to make printed circuits. Two easy methods which produce good results will be discussed in this chapter. The first uses etch-resist transfers; the second is a photographic process.

### Etch-Resist Process

For simple circuits the use of *etch-resist transfers* makes a good-quality printed circuit. The transfers come in sheets that contain lines of various widths, circles, dual in-line pads for ICs, and other patterns. An example of one manufacturer's product is shown in Figure 15-12. The etch-resist material is applied by placing the sheets face down on the copper side of the board and pressing with a smooth, hard object on the part of the sheet

| COMPONENT | LETTER | SYMBOL | PICTORIAL |
|-----------|--------|--------|-----------|
| AMMETER | M |  | 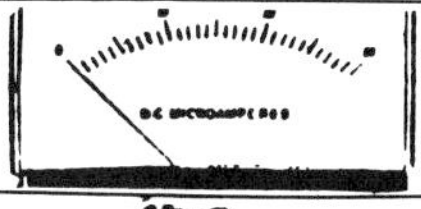 |
| BATTERY | B |  |  |
| CAPACITOR | C |  |  |
| COIL | L |  | 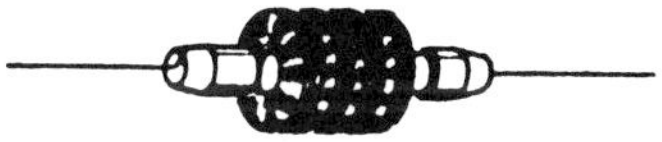 |
| DIODE | D |  |  |
| ELECTRICAL JACK | J |  |  |
| ELECTRICAL PLUG | |  |  |
| FUSE | F |  |  |
| INTEGRATED CIRCUIT | IC or U | |  |
| LAMP | LP |  |  |
| LIGHT-EMITTING DIODE | LED |  |  |
| NEON LAMP | LP |  |  |

**Figure 15–8.** Components and their symbols

| COMPONENT | LETTER | SYMBOL | PICTORIAL |
|-----------|--------|--------|-----------|
| POTENTIOMETER | R | 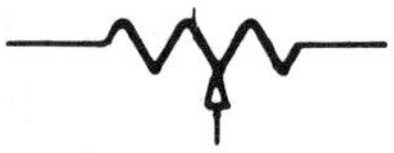 |  |
| RESISTOR | R |  |  |
| SOLAR CELL | SC |  |  |
| SPEAKER | SP |  | 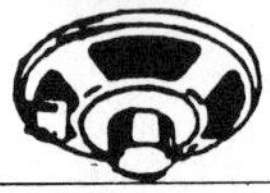 |
| SWITCH (Push button) | SW-PB |  |  |
| SWITCH (Toggle) | SW |  |  |
| TRANSFORMER | T |  |  |
| TRANSISTOR | Q |  |  |
| VOLTMETER | M |  |  |
| | | | |
| | | | |
| | | | |

**Figure 15-8.** Continued

| TERM | SYMBOL |
|------|--------|
| CLOCK PULSE | ⎍ |
| KILO | k |
| MEGA | M or MEG |
| MICRO | μ |
| MILLI | m |
| SINE WAVE | ∽ |
| SQUARE WAVE | ⊓⏟ |
| + VOLTS DC | + V DC |

**Figure 15-9.** Symbols for terms used in schematic diagrams

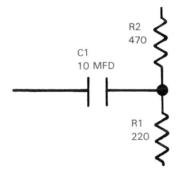

R2
470

C1
10 MFD

R1
220

**Figure 15-10.** How values are given on a schematic

PARTS LIST

C1—.1 MFD 50V
C2—10 MFD 50V
C3—.02 MFD
D1, D2—1N4004
D3—1N 914
IC1—LM 317
IC2—7400 NAND Gate
IC3—74193
LED 1, 2, 3, 4—Jumbo
R1—150 kΩ
R2—270 Ω
R3—10 kΩ

**Figure 15-11.** Parts list

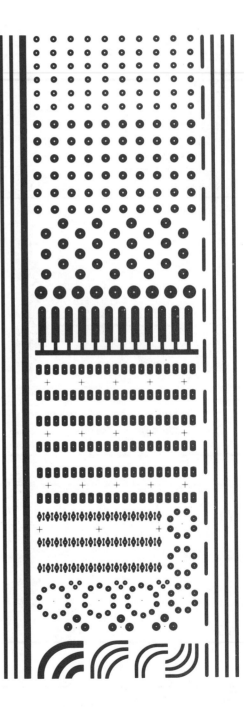

**Figure 15-12.** Etch-resist transfer sheet
(courtesy of Tandy Corporation)

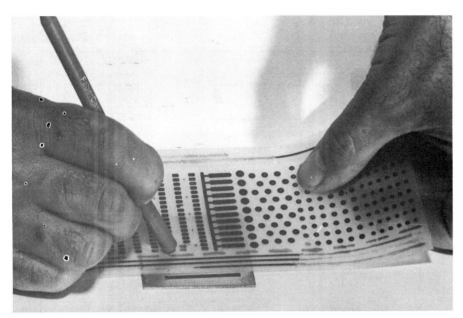

**Figure 15-13.** Pattern being transferred from transfer sheet to copper (courtesy of Tandy Corporation)

you want transferred. Do not allow the transfer sheet to move when applying the pads for an IC, or the spacing between pins will be incorrect. Figure 15–13 shows a pattern being transferred to the copper. In some cases where a circuit board pattern is unavailable, it is necessary to design the PC board layout before using the etch-resist transfers.

## Designing a PC Board Layout

When designing a PC board layout, you must follow the schematic for the circuit closely so that you connect all components properly. Whenever possible, PC board layouts should be designed so that pin 1 of each IC is to the upper left when the IC is mounted vertically. Pin 1 should be to the lower left of all of the horizontally mounted ICs, Figure 15–14.

There must be a pad (circular or rectangular-shaped copper area) for each lead of each component. Narrow strips of copper called *traces* are used to make connections between pads. The size of the pads and the traces are determined by the amount of current they must handle. For most digital

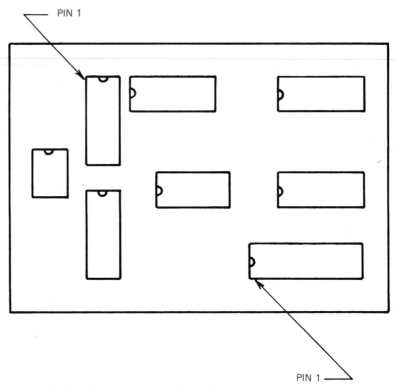

**Figure 15-14.** Alignment of pin 1 is to the lower left on horizontally placed ICs and to the top left on vertically placed ICs.

logic circuits 3/32-inch or 1/8-inch pads and 1/16-inch to 1/8-inch traces or larger work well. You should allow about 1/8-inch spacing between traces.

To keep the traces from crossing each other, use components to bridge across them, as shown in Figure 15-15. If necessary, use a jumper wire to bridge across a trace, as shown in Figure 15-16. When laying out the connections for an IC, remember that it is possible to lay traces between the two rows of pads, Figure 15-17. To properly position all of the pads, bend the leads of the components into the shape they will be when mounted in the circuit, and use them as a guide, as shown in Figure 15-18.

Be sure to provide pads for all external connecting wires such as power supply leads, meter leads, etc. Also, you may wish to use transfer letters to

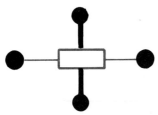

**Figure 15-15.** Component used to bridge across a trace

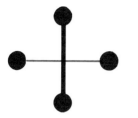

**Figure 15-17.** Trace running between rows of pads

**Figure 15-16.** Jumper wire used to bridge across a trace. (Jumper wire should be placed on component side of the board.)

put your name, the date, identification of components, and a name for the device on the PCB. However, be certain that none of the lettering will interfere with the circuit operation.

Components are mounted on the opposite side of the PC board from the copper so that they will not interfere with the process of soldering. The fact that the components are on the side opposite the copper creates a problem. The pins or leads of components are placed in just the opposite position of where they would be if they were mounted on the same side as

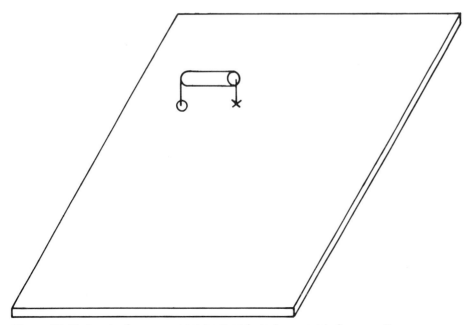

**Figure 15-18.** Leads of a component bent and used as a guide for mounting

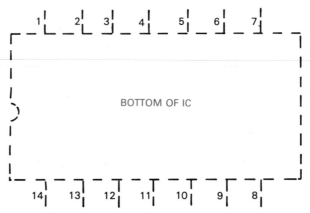

**Figure 15-19.** IC shown from copper side of PCB. Notice pin location is reversed.

the copper. Figure 15-19 shows how component leads are reversed on opposite sides of the board.

One way to solve this problem when designing a PC board layout is to use a fairly transparent tracing paper. Draw a sketch of the layout using the actual components for spacing and proper pin position. At this point, design the PC board layout as if the components were to be on the same side as the copper. When the layout is finished, turn over the tracing paper, and lay it on a piece of carbon paper that is positioned on the copper side of the board. Go over the lines with a hard pencil or ballpoint pen, and the carbon paper will transfer the circuit layout pattern to the copper on the PCB. Follow the pattern in applying the etch-resist material. Figure 15-20 shows how the tracing paper and carbon are used. As you can see from the figure, the numbers and letters are a little difficult to read because they are backwards, but the positions for their pads are correct.

**Etching the Circuit Board.**    When all of the transfers have been applied and pressed down firmly, the board is ready to etch. Ready-to-use liquid etchants do a good job of etching copper, but they can be dangerous. Be sure to follow the directions that come with the etchant. Wear safety glasses when using etchant, and avoid getting any liquid on your skin. If any of the etchant does come into contact with your skin, wash it off immediately.

Use enough etchant to entirely cover the board. It is best to do only one board at a time to avoid boards bumping each other and losing the

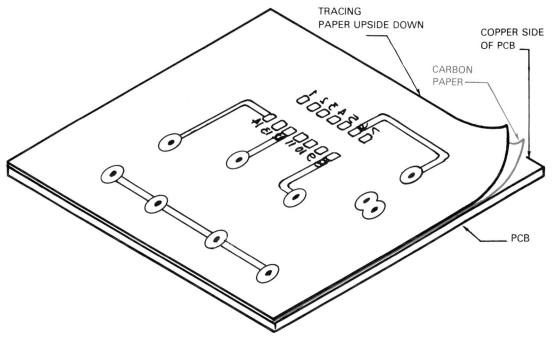

**Figure 15-20.** Reversed circuit pattern being transferred to copper side of PCB

transfers. The time it takes to etch a board is dependent upon the size of the board and the strength of the etchant. The etching process can be speeded up by gently agitating the etchant or by heating the etchant to a little above room temperature. Do not allow the PCB to etch too long because the etchant will undermine the etch-resist and may cause a break in the trace, Figure 15–21.

As soon as the copper not covered by the etch-resist material has been etched away, remove the board immediately from the etchant and thoroughly wash it with water. When the board has dried, use steel wool to remove the etch-resist and to buff the remaining copper until it is shiny.

## Photographic Process

The other method of making the PCB is suitable for more complex circuits. It is a photographic process, but it does not require sophisticated photographic equipment. The advantage of this process is that it makes use

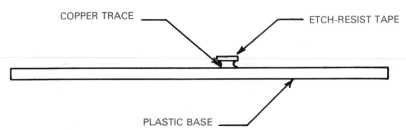

**Figure 15-21.** Overetched printed circuit board. Notice the trace is undermined.

of a circuit board layout that has already been designed. The circuit board designs are found in magazine articles about projects and in project books.

The circuit layout may be either a positive or a negative. Either will work well. However, the photosensitive etch-resist material on the circuit board must be positive-acting for positive circuit layouts and negative-acting for negative circuit layouts. Positive and negative circuit layouts appear in Figure 15-22.

The circuit layout that you find in a magazine article or project book should be actual size. If it is not, use a copy machine to reduce or enlarge the circuit layout. Inspect the copy and blacken with a felt-tip pen any light spots in the black area of the copy. Cover with whiteout any unwanted black spots in the white area of the copy. From this good black-and-white copy, make a transparency using the transparency maker that is available in most schools. You may need to try various darkness settings to get a transparency with no areas burned out or bled together, Figure 15-23.

A transparency may be touched up by using a permanent black marker to fill in burned-out areas and by using a sharp knife to carefully remove unwanted black areas. Once you have made a good transparency, keep it clean and lint free by storing it in a manila folder or large envelope. Be sure to label the folder or envelope so that you can identify it easily in the future.

Circuit boards that are already coated with a photo-etch-resist material can be purchased, or you may make your own board by applying photo-etch-resist to a copper-clad circuit board. If you coat your own boards, follow the directions provided with the material, and work in a well-ventilated area. Coating (sometimes called "sensitizing") your own boards is less expensive than purchasing them already sensitized, but it is difficult to get the same quality.

Photosensitized boards must be exposed to ultraviolet light through the transparency of the circuit layout. Two safe sources of ultraviolet light

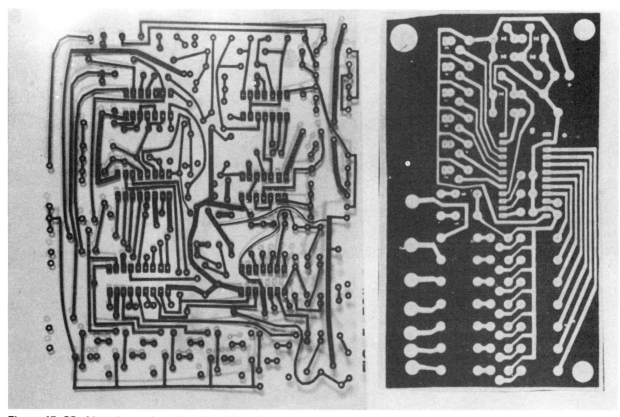

**Figure 15-22.** *Negative and positive circuit layouts*

are the sun and an overhead transparency projector. The clean transparency should be aligned to the photosensitized board in a room that is lighted with only photographic-safe lights. The transparency should be placed on the sensitized side of the board so that you can read any printing that might be on it.

When the overhead projector is used for exposure to ultraviolet light, the transparency and the circuit board are placed with the board on top of the glass plate of the projector, as shown in Figure 15-24. A small weight may be placed on top of the circuit board in order to hold the transparency firmly against the glass and circuit board.

If the sun is used for exposure to ultraviolet light, a printmaking frame is ideal for holding the transparency tight against the circuit board. The exposure time varies with the brightness of the light and the sensitivity of

**Figure 15-23.** Transparencies made at different settings. Top transparency is overexposed, center transparency shows some improvement, bottom transparency is the best of the group.

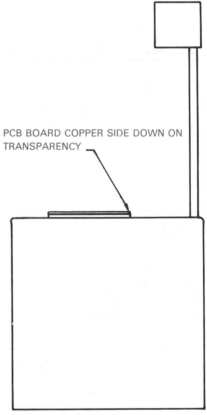

PCB BOARD COPPER SIDE DOWN ON TRANSPARENCY

**Figure 15-24.** Overhead projector used to expose sensitized PCB

the photo-etch-resist material. Follow the manufacturer's recommendations for correct exposure time. After the exposure is complete, follow the manufacturer's developing procedures using the recommended developer. The etching process and cleaning after etching are the same as described earlier in this chapter.

The next step is to drill the holes in the PCB. The holes are for the component leads to extend from the component side of the board to the copper side. Components used in digital electronic circuits can be small in size because they usually do not have to carry very much current. Thus the holes in the PCB can be fairly small in diameter. Drill bits from #60 (.040 diameter) to 1/16 drill bit (.062 diameter) are appropriate for most digital electronic work.

Before drilling, use a center punch to give the drill bit a starting point. Using the punch is especially critical when drilling the holes for the pins of an IC socket. Without the small identation to start in, the drill bit could wander around on the surface, and you may end up with holes that are not aligned, as in Figure 15–25. It would be difficult to start the pins of the IC socket into poorly aligned holes. Lay the PCB on a flat surface, and do not strike the center punch very hard because circuit boards can be easily broken. Use a high-speed drill and make sure that the drill bit does not hit any metal after going into the board because small bits can be easily broken.

**Figure 15-25.** Misaligned holes in IC pads

## Mounting Components

Remember that components are mounted on the side of the PC board that is not the copper side. Components that have no polarity, such as resistors and capacitors (other than electrolytic capacitors), should be mounted so that you can read identifying marks easily from left to right or bottom to top as shown in Figure 15–26. As you can see from the figure, resistors have no written value, but they do have several bands. These bands are of different colors and are used to indicate the values. Figure 15–27 provides a resistor color-code chart so you can determine the value of a resistor.

Transistors, diodes, and electrolytic capacitors should be mounted so that their leads connect to the proper point in the circuit because they could be damaged by connecting them incorrectly. Figure 15–28 shows how the positive and negative leads may be identified on diodes and electrolytic capacitors. Figure 15–29 shows some of the ways to identify transistor leads. If you are not sure, always find out the proper way to mount a component rather than take a chance on mounting it the wrong way.

## Soldering

The main cause of projects not working properly when first assembled is poor solder connections. Even beginners can make good solder joints if they follow the proper procedures.

The selection of solder is important because the melting temperature can vary nearly 100 degrees Fahrenheit depending upon its makeup. Solder is an alloy (a mixture of two or more metals that make a metal with different characteristics than either of the original metals) of tin and lead. A combination of 63 percent tin and 37 percent lead is the mixture that has the lowest melting point—approximately 361 degrees; 60/40 solder (60

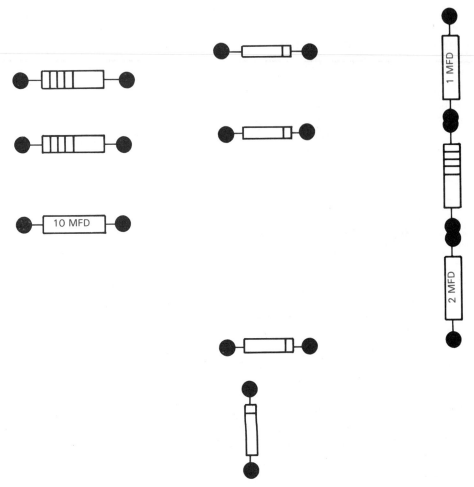

**Figure 15-26.** Correct mounting of components such as resistors and nonelectrolytic capacitors

percent tin and 40 percent lead) melts at 375 degrees; 50/50 at 415 degrees, and 40/60 at 455 degrees. The higher the percentage of tin, the more expensive the solder. Since many electronic components are easily damaged by too much heat, solder with a low melting temperature is best to use. Electronics work most often uses 60/40 solder.

Solder used in electronics work should be in the form of a thin wire. A small gauge of wire solder, such as 20 or 22 gauge, works well for soldering on printed circuit boards. The small-diameter wire makes it easier to apply

| COLOR | 1ST DIGIT | 2ND DIGIT | ZEROS ADDED | TOLERANCE (PERCENT) |
|---|---|---|---|---|
| BLACK | 0 | 0 | | |
| BROWN | 1 | 1 | 0 | |
| RED | 2 | 2 | 00 | |
| ORANGE | 3 | 3 | 000 | |
| YELLOW | 4 | 4 | 0,000 | |
| GREEN | 5 | 5 | 00,000 | |
| BLUE | 6 | 6 | 000,000 | |
| VIOLET | 7 | 7 | 0,000,000 | |
| GRAY | 8 | 8 | 00,000,000 | |
| WHITE | 9 | 9 | 000,000,000 | |
| GOLD | | | .1 | ±5 |
| SILVER | | | .01 | ±10 |
| NONE | | | | ±20 |
| | BAND 1 | BAND 2 | BAND 3 | BAND 4 |

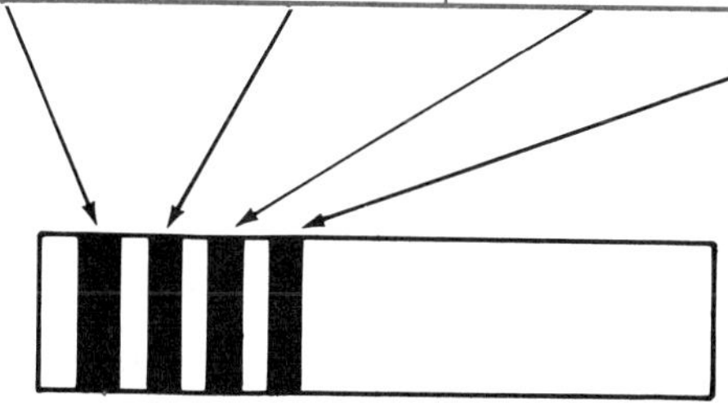

RESISTOR

**Figure 15-27.** Color code chart for resistors

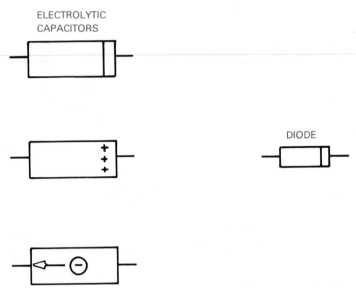

**Figure 15-28.** Identification of leads on diodes and electrolytic capacitors

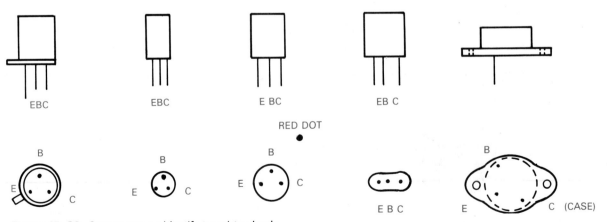

**Figure 15-29.** Some ways to identify transistor leads

solder to just the right spot when working on a circuit that has extremely close connections. Also smaller-diameter solder wire does not require as much heat as a larger-diameter wire, and less heat is applied to the circuit. Figure 15–30 shows single-core and multi-core solder wire. The solder should also contain one or more cores of *flux*. The purpose of the flux is to clean off the thin film of oxide that forms on the metals to be soldered (such as copper). The flux also forms a protective coating that keeps the oxide from forming during the soldering process. The fluxes used for electronics work should be rosin-type rather than acid-type. Acid-type flux is very corrosive and causes a high resistance to form between the materials that are connected. It should never be used for any type of electrical work.

**Soldering Irons.**  For printed circuit boards, use a small soldering iron called a soldering pencil. The wattage of a soldering pencil determines the amount of heat it can produce. A wattage of from 15 to 40 watts is suitable for use on most printed circuit boards. Figure 15–31 shows several different shapes of tips that can be used with soldering pencils. Tips for most PCB work should be 1/8 or 1/16 inch in width. These widths are large enough to allow the surface area to transfer heat effectively, but are small enough to fit into tight areas. For maximum heat transfer, tips should be kept clean by wiping them on a damp sponge when an oxide layer forms on them. Nickel-plated and iron-plated tips do not corrode as quickly as unplated tips.

**Making a Good Solder Connection.**  Once you have chosen the correct rosin-core solder and the right wattage pencil and tip (which must be clean), then clean the surfaces that you want the solder to stick to. PCBs should be buffed until shiny with either steel wool or sandpaper. If component leads are tarnished or corroded, they should also be cleaned.

Next, apply heat to both surfaces that you wish to solder. Both items to be soldered need to be heated to approximately the same temperature because molten solder will actually flow over a heated surface to the hottest spot. To raise the temperature of both surfaces to the same level, it may be necessary to apply more heat to the larger area by having more of the tip of the soldering pencil in contact with it than is in contact with the smaller area. The materials to be soldered should get hot enough so that when the

**Figure 15–30.** *Single-core and multi-core solder wire*

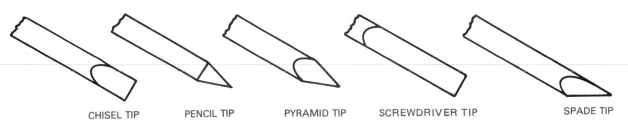

CHISEL TIP          PENCIL TIP          PYRAMID TIP          SCREWDRIVER TIP                    SPADE TIP

**Figure 15-31.** Various tips for soldering pencils

solder is held against them next to the soldering pencil tip, the solder will melt. If the materials to be soldered are not hot enough to melt the solder, do not melt the solder by holding it against the solder pencil tip because the solder will usually not stick to the desired surfaces. Instead, it will stay on the pencil tip or roll off onto the surfaces to be soldered without adhering to them well enough to make a good electrical connection. Such a connection is called a cold solder joint and is to be avoided.

When soldering on a PC board, the entire pad should always be covered with solder, and the solder should go up the component lead a short distance. To cover an area of the pad that is not covered, move the soldering pencil to that area and apply more solder if necessary. Heat should be applied to a PC board only long enough to make a good solder connection. Excessive heat can cause the copper to pull away from the base material. Figure 15-32 shows correct and incorrect solder joints.

## Project Assembly

Some components are easily ruined by too much heat. To protect these components, a special tool called a *heat sink* or alligator clips can be used to draw the heat away from the component. The alligator clips or heat sinks are placed on the component lead between the component and solder connection as shown in Figure 15-33. Transistors and diodes are heat sensitive and should be mounted about 3/16 of an inch above the board to allow enough space to apply a heat sink during soldering.

ICs are also heat sensitive. To avoid overheating an IC and ruining it, place the IC in an IC socket. IC sockets look a lot like ICs and are usually marked in such a way that you can tell which pin is pin 1, Figure 15-34. Another advantage of using an IC socket is that if for any reason you have to change an IC, you do not have to unsolder and resolder it.

Resistors and capacitors are not easily ruined by heat and thus do not need to have a heat sink placed on them during soldering. They should be

## INCORRECT

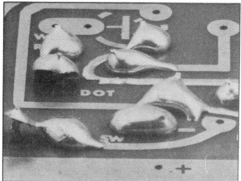

These solder connections are incorrect and were caused by excessive soldering iron temperature, too long a heating period and too much solder. Notice that the copper islands are covered with large blobs of excess solder. Also the copper foil has lifted (separated) from the circuit board due to too much heat, which was caused by an iron with too high a wattage, or by a prolonged heating period. These types of connections can be corrected by using a 30-50 watt iron, a short heating period and a small amount of solder.

## CORRECT

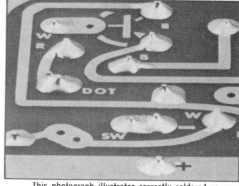

This photograph illustrates correctly soldered connections on a printed circuit board. Good solder connections have a smooth bright appearance and an evenly contoured fillet on both the component lead and copper foil island. Standard soldering practices apply to p.c. soldering: cleanliness, proper temperature and heating period, and 60/40 rosin core solder. Greater care must be taken to prevent overheating which can cause damage to semiconductors or the copper foil.

## FRACTURE

These incorrect soldering connections are called FRAC-TURED CONNECTIONS. This was caused by the components being moved during the solder freeze. This movement disturbs the formation of smooth and well-contoured solder connections. These can be corrected by reheating the connections. Be sure that the component leads do not move until the solder has solidified. Remember a good connection has a bright appearance and a smoothly contoured fillet.

## BRIDGE

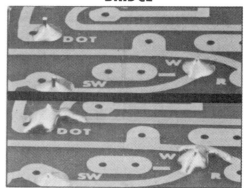

The above photographs show the same circuit board. Notice, in the bottom photograph that the solder connections have accidentally bridged between two adjacent copper island conductors. This was caused by using an iron with a large soldering surface, applying too much solder or poor circuit design. To correct a bridge connection, carefully reheat the connection and allow the excess solder to flow onto the soldering iron for removal.

**Figure 15–32.** Correct and incorrect soldering joints (courtesy of Graymark International Inc.)

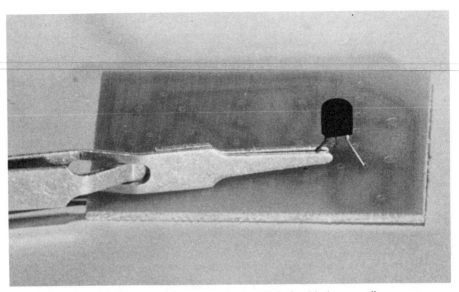

**Figure 15–33.** Heat sink used between component and soldering pencil

mounted by placing their leads full length in the proper holes and then bending them over.

After the components are soldered in, the extra leads can be cut off at the solder joints. As you may remember, it is always necessary to wear safety glasses when soldering, and to avoid contact with the hot soldering pencil tip and fresh solder joints.

## Desoldering

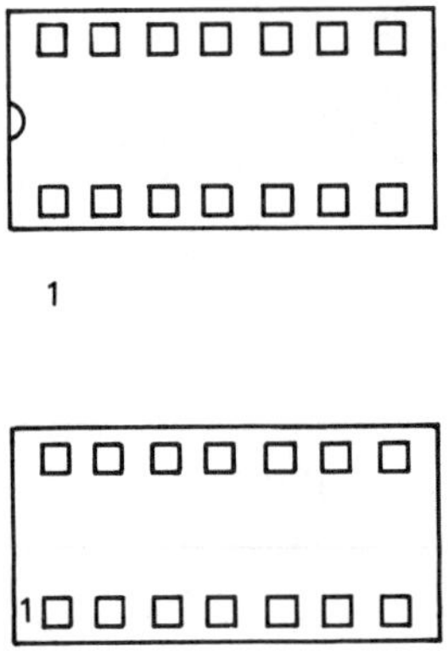

If a component needs to be removed from a PC board because it is bad or was placed in the wrong location, the connections of the component to the PC board must be desoldered. One way of removing solder is to use a vacuum to pull molten solder from the connection. Two vacuum-type desoldering tools appear in Figure 15–35. To use the bulb-type tool, squeeze the bulb then let it expand quickly in order to form a vacuum. The molten solder will flow in through the tip. The other tool shown in Figure 15–35 uses a spring-loaded plunger inside a cylinder that creates a vacuum when the spring is released, forcing the plunger through the cylinder.

Another method of removing solder is to use *capillary action* (the tendency of a liquid to flow upward into a very small tube) to pull solder away from the connection. A braided copper strip is placed on the solder

**Figure 15–34.** IC sockets

**Figure 15–35.** Two vacuum-type desoldering tools

connection, and a hot soldering pencil is placed on the braid. The heated copper draws the solder into itself. Figure 15–36 shows copper braid being used to remove solder.

In desoldering as in soldering, it is important to avoid overheating the components or the PC board.

## Mounting the Project

When the components are all mounted and all external connections such as leads for the power supply are made, the circuit should be tested. If it works properly, it should be mounted in an appropriate case. Many different sizes and styles of metal or plastic cases are available. For most battery-operated projects, it is not necessary to leave space for air circulation to cool the circuit, and a case just large enough to fit the circuit board and all necessary switches, batteries, etc., will be adequate.

A good way to mount the circuit board securely in a case is to use spacers in at least three locations and preferably four locations on the circuit board. Figure 15–37 shows spacers being used to mount the circuit board and also small feet attached to the bottom of the case to allow clearance for the heads of the screws holding the circuit board. Be certain

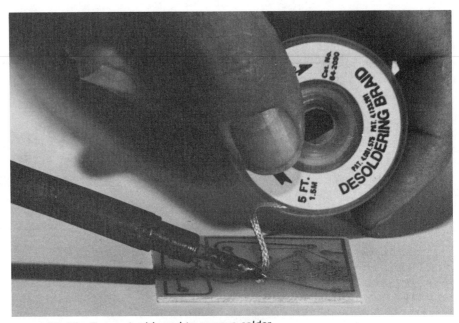

**Figure 15-36.** Copper braid used to remove solder

that any sharp edges or corners are removed from metal cases. The cases may be covered with contact paper to make them look more attractive. Components that are mounted on the case such as switches, lamps, etc., should be labeled. Transfer letters work very nicely for lettering, but they should be sprayed with clear lacquer to make them more permanent.

## SUMMARY

In this chapter you learned to read a schematic diagram by correctly identifying component symbols and determining how the components are

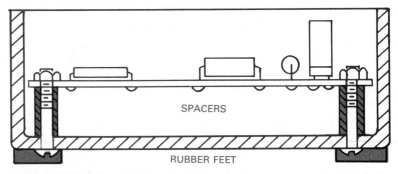

**Figure 15-37.** Mounting the circuit board using spacers and rubber feet

**Figure 15–38**

connected to one another. You also learned how to make a printed circuit board using either the etch-resist transfer method or the photographic method. Finally, you learned the procedures for mounting and soldering components on a circuit board and assembling the entire project into a case.

## REVIEW QUESTIONS

1. Explain the difference between a project built from scratch and one built from a kit.
2. If the two symbols shown in Figure 15–38 appear on the same schematic, would you expect there to be an electrical connection between them?
3. Why are the pins not arranged in numerical order on schematic diagrams?
4. Of the two methods of making PC boards discussed in this chapter, which should be used for complex circuits?
5. What type of flux core should be used for electrical work?
6. State the percentage of lead and tin in 60/40 solder.
7. List three components that could be damaged by excessive heat during soldering.
8. Other than ruining a component, what other problem could occur with the circuit board when desoldering?

## SUGGESTED ACTIVITIES

1. Look through recent issues of electronics magazines, and find a project that you would like to build. Using either the etch-resist-transfer method or photo method, make a printed circuit board for the project.
2. Acquire the necessary components, build the project, and install it in a suitable case.

# APPENDIX

## *READING SPECIFICATION SHEETS*

Specification sheets are used by circuit designers to make sure that the ICs used in a device will coordinate with each other and with other components. Study the following examples to find such information as supply voltage, high-level output current, etc., for the 7408 IC.

The 54 Family of ICs is used by the military. As you may have noticed, these ICs have a wider temperature operating range and are built to be more reliable than the 74 Family.

In order to use the specification sheets (commonly called "spec sheets"), study the following pages and refer back to them as necessary. The specification sheets shown are from Texas Instruments Incorporated, Dallas, Texas.

# TTL
# EXPLANATION OF FUNCTION TABLES

## EXPLANATION OF FUNCTION TABLES

The following symbols are now being used in function tables on TI data sheets:

| | | |
|---|---|---|
| H | = | high level (steady state) |
| L | = | low level (steady state) |
| $\uparrow$ | = | transition from low to high level |
| $\downarrow$ | = | transition from high to low level |
| X | = | irrelevant (any input, including transitions) |
| Z | = | off (high-impedance) state of a 3-state output |
| a..h | = | the level of steady-state inputs at inputs A through H respectively |
| $Q_0$ | = | level of Q before the indicated steady-state input conditions were establsihed |
| $\overline{Q}_0$ | = | complement of $Q_0$ or level of $\overline{Q}$ before the indicated steady-state input conditions were established |
| $Q_n$ | = | level of Q before the most recent active transition indicated by $\downarrow$ or $\uparrow$ |
| ⊓ | = | one high-level pulse |
| ⊔ | = | one low-level pulse |
| TOGGLE | = | each output changes to the complement of its previous level on each active transition indicated by $\downarrow$ or $\uparrow$. |

If, in the input columns, a row contains only the symbols H, L, and/or X, this means the indicated output is valid whenever the input configuration is achieved and regardless of the sequence in which it is achieved. The output persists so long as the input configuration is maintained.

If, in the input columns, a row contains H, L, and/or X together with $\uparrow$ and/or $\downarrow$, this means the output is valid whenever the input configuration is achieved but the transition(s) must occur following the achievement of the steady-state levels. If the output is shown as a level (H, L, $Q_0$, or $\overline{Q}_0$), it persists so long as the steady-state input levels and the levels that terminate indicated transitions are maintained. Unless otherwise indicated, input transitions in the opposite direction to those shown have no effect at the output. (If the output is shown as a pulse, ⊓ or ⊔, the pulse follows the indicated input transition and persists for an interval dependent on the circuit.)

Among the most complex function tables in this book are those of the shift registers. These embody most of the symbols used in any of the function tables, plus more. Below is the function table of a 4-bit bidirectional universal shift register, e.g., type SN74194.

FUNCTION TABLE

| CLEAR | MODE | | CLOCK | SERIAL | | PARALLEL | | | | OUTPUTS | | | |
| | S1 | S0 | | LEFT | RIGHT | A | B | C | D | $Q_A$ | $Q_B$ | $Q_C$ | $Q_D$ |
|---|---|---|---|---|---|---|---|---|---|---|---|---|---|
| L | X | X | X | X | X | X | X | X | X | L | L | L | L |
| H | X | X | L | X | X | X | X | X | X | $Q_{A0}$ | $Q_{B0}$ | $Q_{C0}$ | $Q_{D0}$ |
| H | H | H | ↑ | X | X | a | b | c | d | a | b | c | d |
| H | L | H | ↑ | X | H | X | X | X | X | H | $Q_{An}$ | $Q_{Bn}$ | $Q_{Cn}$ |
| H | L | H | ↑ | X | L | X | X | X | X | L | $Q_{An}$ | $Q_{Bn}$ | $Q_{Cn}$ |
| H | H | L | ↑ | H | X | X | X | X | X | $Q_{Bn}$ | $Q_{Cn}$ | $Q_{Dn}$ | H |
| H | H | L | ↑ | L | X | X | X | X | X | $Q_{Bn}$ | $Q_{Cn}$ | $Q_{Dn}$ | L |
| H | L | L | X | X | X | X | X | X | X | $Q_{A0}$ | $Q_{B0}$ | $Q_{C0}$ | $Q_{D0}$ |

The first line of the table represents a synchronous clearing of the register and says that if clear is low, all four outputs will be reset low regardless of the other inputs. In the following lines, clear is inactive (high) and so has no effect.

The second line shows that so long as the clock input remains low (while clear is high), no other input has any effect and the outputs maintain the levels they assumed before the steady-state combination of clear high and clock low was established. Since on other lines of the table only the rising transition of the clock is shown to be active, the second line implicitly shows that no further change in the outputs will occur while the clock remains high or on the high-to-low transition of the clock.

The third line of the table represents synchronous parallel loading of the register and says that if S1 and S0 are both high then, without regard to the serial input, the data entered at A will be at output $Q_A$, data entered at B will be at $Q_B$, and so forth, following a low-to-high clock transition.

The fourth and fifth lines represent the loading of high- and low-level data, respectively, from the shift-right serial input and the shifting of previously entered data one bit; data previously at $Q_A$ is now at $Q_B$, the previous levels of $Q_B$ and $Q_C$ are now at $Q_C$ and $Q_D$ respectively, and the data previously at $Q_D$ is no longer in the register. This entry of serial data and shift takes place on the low-to-high transition of the clock when S1 is low and S0 is high and the levels at inputs A through D have no effect.

The sixth and seventh lines represent the loading of high- and low-level data, respectively, from the shift-left serial input and the shifting of previously entered data one bit; data previously at $Q_B$ is now at $Q_A$, the previous levels of $Q_C$ and $Q_D$ are now at $Q_B$ and $Q_C$, respectively, and the data previously at $Q_A$ is no longer in the register. This entry of serial data and shift takes place on the low-to-high transition of the clock when S1 is high and S0 is low and the levels at inputs A through D have no effect.

The last line shows that as long as both mode inputs are low, no other input has any effect and, as in the second line, the outputs maintain the levels they assumed before the steady-state combination of clear high and both mode inputs low was established.

# POSITIVE-AND GATES WITH TOTEM-POLE OUTPUTS

## recommended operating conditions

| 54 FAMILY / 74 FAMILY | | SERIES 54 / SERIES 74 '08 MIN | NOM | MAX | SERIES 54H / SERIES 74H 'H11, 'H21 MIN | NOM | MAX | SERIES 54LS / SERIES 74LS 'LS08, 'LS11, 'LS21 MIN | NOM | MAX | SERIES 54S / SERIES 74S 'S08, 'S11 MIN | NOM | MAX | UNIT |
|---|---|---|---|---|---|---|---|---|---|---|---|---|---|---|
| Supply Voltage, $V_{CC}$ | 54 Family | 4.5 | 5 | 5.5 | 4.5 | 5 | 5.5 | 4.5 | 5 | 5.5 | 4.5 | 5 | 5.5 | V |
| | 74 Family | 4.75 | 5 | 5.25 | 4.75 | 5 | 5.25 | 4.75 | 5 | 5.25 | 4.75 | 5 | 5.25 | |
| High-level output current, $I_{OH}$ | | | | −800 | | | −500 | | | −400 | | | −1000 | µA |
| Low-level output current, $I_{OL}$ | 54 Family | | | 16 | | | 20 | | | 4 | | | 20 | mA |
| | 74 Family | | | 16 | | | 20 | | | 8 | | | 20 | |
| Operating free-air temperature, $T_A$ | 54 Family | −55 | | 125 | −55 | | 125 | −55 | | 125 | −55 | | 125 | °C |
| | 74 Family | 0 | | 70 | 0 | | 70 | 0 | | 70 | 0 | | 70 | |

## electrical characteristics over recommended operating free-air temperature range (unless otherwise noted)

| PARAMETER | TEST FIGURE | TEST CONDITIONS[†] | SERIES 54 / SERIES 74 '08 MIN | TYP[‡] | MAX | SERIES 54H / SERIES 74H 'H11, 'H21 MIN | TYP[‡] | MAX | SERIES 54LS / SERIES 74LS 'LS08, 'LS11, 'LS21 MIN | TYP[‡] | MAX | SERIES 54S / SERIES 74S 'S08, 'S11 MIN | TYP[‡] | MAX | UNIT |
|---|---|---|---|---|---|---|---|---|---|---|---|---|---|---|---|
| $V_{IH}$ High-level input voltage | 1, 2 | | 2 | | | 2 | | | 2 | | | 2 | | | V |
| $V_{IL}$ Low-level input voltage | 1, 2 | 54 Family | | | 0.8 | | | 0.8 | | | 0.7 | | | 0.8 | V |
| | | 74 Family | | | 0.8 | | | 0.8 | | | 0.8 | | | 0.8 | |
| $V_{IK}$ Input clamp voltage | 3 | $V_{CC}$ = MIN, $I_I$ = § | | | −1.5 | | | −1.5 | | | −1.5 | | | −1.2 | V |
| $V_{OH}$ High-level output voltage | 1 | $V_{CC}$ = MIN, $V_{IH}$ = 2 V, $I_{OH}$ = MAX | 2.4 | 3.4 | | 2.4 | 3.4 | | 2.5 | 3.4 | | 2.5 | 3.4 | | V |
| | | | 2.4 | 3.4 | | 2.4 | 3.4 | | 2.7 | 3.4 | | 2.7 | 3.4 | | |
| $V_{OL}$ Low-level output voltage | 2 | $V_{CC}$ = MIN, $I_{OL}$ = MAX | 0.2 | | 0.4 | 0.15 | | 0.3 | 0.25 | | 0.4 | | | 0.5 | V |
| | | $V_{IH}$ = 2 V | 0.2 | | 0.4 | 0.2 | | 0.4 | 0.35 | | 0.5 | | | 0.5 | |
| | | Series 74LS $I_{OL}$ = 4 mA | | | | | | | 0.25 | | 0.4 | | | | |
| $I_I$ Input current at maximum input voltage | 4 | $V_I$ = 5.5 V | | | 1 | | | 0.1 | | | 0.1 | | | 1 | mA |
| | | $V_I$ = 7 V | | | | | | | | | | | | | |
| $I_{IH}$ High-level input current | 4 | $V_{CC}$ = MAX; $V_{IH}$ = 2.4 V; $V_{IH}$ = 2.7 V | | | 40 | | | 50 | | | 20 | | | 50 | µA |
| $I_{IL}$ Low-level input current | 5 | $V_{CC}$ = MAX; $V_{IL}$ = 0.4 V; $V_{IL}$ = 0.5 V | | | −1.6 | | | −2 | | | −0.4 | | | −2 | mA |
| $I_{OS}$ Short circuit output current◆ | 6 | $V_{CC}$ = MAX | −20 | | −55 | −40 | | −100 | −20 | | −100 | −40 | | −100 | mA |
| | | | −18 | | −55 | −40 | | −100 | −20 | | −100 | −40 | | −100 | |
| $I_{CC}$ Supply current | 7 | $V_{CC}$ = MAX | | | | | | | | | | See table on next page | | | mA |

[†]For conditions shown as MIN or MAX, use the appropriate values specified under recommended operating conditions.
[‡]All typical values are at $V_{CC}$ = 25°C.
§ $I_I$ = −12 mA for SN54'/SN74', −8 mA for SN54H'/SN74H', and −18 mA for SN54LS'/SN74LS' and SN54S'/SN74S'.
◆Not more than one output should be shorted at a time, and for SN54H'/SN74H', SN54LS'/SN74LS' and SN54S'/SN74S', duration of output short circuit should not exceed one second.

### recommended operating conditions

| | 54 FAMILY / 74 FAMILY | SERIES 54 / SERIES 74 '32 | | | SERIES 54LS / SERIES 74LS 'LS32 | | | SERIES 54S / SERIES 74S 'S32 | | | UNIT |
|---|---|---|---|---|---|---|---|---|---|---|---|
| | | MIN | NOM | MAX | MIN | NOM | MAX | MIN | NOM | MAX | |
| Supply voltage, $V_{CC}$ | 54 Family | 4.5 | 5 | 5.5 | 4.5 | 5 | 5.5 | 4.5 | 5 | 5.25 | V |
| | 74 Family | 4.75 | 5 | 5.25 | 4.75 | 5 | 5.25 | 4.75 | 5 | 5.25 | |
| High-level output current, $I_{OH}$ | 74 Family | | | −800 | | | −400 | | | −1000 | µA |
| Low-level output current, $I_{OL}$ | 54 Family | | | 16 | | | 8 | | | 20 | mA |
| | 74 Family | | | 16 | | | 8 | | | 20 | |
| Operating free-air temperature, $T_A$ | 54 Family | −55 | | 125 | −55 | | 125 | −55 | | 125 | °C |
| | 74 Family | 0 | | 70 | 0 | | 70 | 0 | | 70 | |

### electrical characteristics over recommended free-air temperature range (unless otherwise noted)

| PARAMETER | TEST FIGURE | TEST CONDITIONS† | | SERIES 54 / SERIES 74 '32 | | | SERIES 54LS / SERIES 74LS 'LS32 | | | SERIES 54S / SERIES 74S 'S32 | | | UNIT |
|---|---|---|---|---|---|---|---|---|---|---|---|---|---|
| | | | | MIN | TYP‡ | MAX | MIN | TYP‡ | MAX | MIN | TYP‡ | MAX | |
| $V_{IH}$ High-level input voltage | 1, 2 | | | 2 | | | 2 | | | 2 | | | V |
| $V_{IL}$ Low-level input voltage | 1, 2 | 54 Family | | | | 0.8 | | | 0.7 | | | 0.8 | V |
| | | 74 Family | | | | 0.8 | | | 0.8 | | | 0.8 | |
| $V_{IK}$ Input clamp voltage | 3 | $V_{CC}$ = MIN, $I_I$ = § | | | | −1.5 | | | −1.5 | | | −1.2 | V |
| $V_{OH}$ High-level output voltage | 1 | $V_{CC}$ = MIN, $V_{IH}$ = 2 V, $I_{OH}$ = MAX | 54 Family | 2.4 | 3.4 | | 2.5 | 3.4 | | 2.5 | 3.4 | | V |
| | | | 74 Family | 2.4 | 3.4 | | 2.7 | 3.4 | | 2.7 | 3.4 | | |
| $V_{OL}$ Low-level output voltage | 2 | $V_{CC}$ = MIN, $V_{IL}$ = $V_{IL}$ max, $I_{OL}$ = MAX | 54 Family | | 0.2 | 0.4 | | 0.25 | 0.4 | | | 0.5 | V |
| | | | 74 Family | | 0.2 | 0.4 | | 0.35 | 0.5 | | | 0.5 | |
| | | $I_{OL}$ = 4 mA | Series 74LS | | | | | 0.25 | 0.4 | | | | |
| $I_I$ Input current at maximum input voltage | 4 | $V_{CC}$ = MAX | $V_I$ = 5.5 V | | | 1 | | | 0.1 | | | 1 | mA |
| | | | $V_I$ = 7 V | | | | | | | | | | |
| $I_{IH}$ High-level input current | 4 | $V_{CC}$ = MAX | $V_{IH}$ = 2.4 V | | | 40 | | | 20 | | | 50 | µA |
| | | | $V_{IH}$ = 2.7 V | | | | | | | | | | |
| $I_{IL}$ Low-level input current | 5 | $V_{CC}$ = MAX | $V_{IL}$ = 0.4 V | | | −1.6 | | | −0.4 | | | −2 | mA |
| | | | $V_{IL}$ = 0.5 V | | | | | | | | | | |
| $I_{OS}$ Short-circuit output current◆ | 6 | $V_{CC}$ = MAX | 54 Family | −20 | | −55 | −20 | | −100 | −40 | | −100 | mA |
| | | | 74 Family | −18 | | −55 | −20 | | −100 | −40 | | −100 | |
| $I_{CC}$ Supply current | 7 | $V_{CC}$ = MAX | Total, outputs high | | 15 | 22 | | 3.1 | 6.2 | | 18 | 32 | mA |
| | | $V_{CC}$ = MAX | Total, outputs low | | 23 | 38 | | 4.9 | 9.8 | | 38 | 68 | |
| | | $V_{CC}$ = 5 V, 50% duty cycle | Average per gate | | 4.75 | | | 1.0 | | | 7 | | |

† For conditions shown as MIN or MAX, use the appropriate value specified under recommended operating conditions.
‡ All typical values are at $V_{CC}$ = 5 V, $T_A$ = 25°C.
§ $I_I$ = −12 mA for SN54'/SN74' and −18 mA for SN54LS'/SN74LS' and SN54S'/SN74S'.
◆ Not more than one output should be shorted at a time, and for SN54LS'/SN74LS' and SN54S'/SN74S', duration of the short-circuit should be less than one second.

# POSITIVE-NOR GATES WITH TOTEM-POLE OUTPUTS

## recommended operating conditions

| 54 FAMILY / 74 FAMILY | | SERIES 54 / SERIES 74 '02 | | | SERIES 54 / SERIES 74 '25, '27 | | | SERIES 54L / SERIES 74L 'L02 | | | SERIES 54LS / SERIES 74LS 'LS02, 'LS27 | | | SERIES 54S / SERIES 74S 'S02, 'S260 | | | UNIT |
|---|---|---|---|---|---|---|---|---|---|---|---|---|---|---|---|---|---|
| | | MIN | NOM | MAX | MIN | NOM | MAX | MIN | NOM | MAX | MIN | NOM | MAX | MIN | NOM | MAX | |
| Supply voltage, $V_{CC}$ | 54 Family | 4.5 | 5 | 5.5 | 4.5 | 5 | 5.5 | 4.5 | 5 | 5.5 | 4.5 | 5 | 5.5 | 4.5 | 5 | 5.5 | V |
| | 74 Family | 4.75 | 5 | 5.25 | 4.75 | 5 | 5.25 | 4.75 | 5 | 5.25 | 4.75 | 5 | 5.25 | 4.75 | 5 | 5.25 | |
| High-level output current, $I_{OH}$ | 54 Family | | | -400 | | | -800 | | | -100 | | | -400 | | | -1000 | µA |
| | 74 Family | | | -400 | | | -800 | | | -200 | | | -400 | | | -1000 | |
| Low-level output current, $I_{OL}$ | 54 Family | | | 16 | | | 16 | | | 2 | | | 4 | | | 20 | mA |
| | 74 Family | | | 16 | | | 16 | | | 3.6 | | | 8 | | | 20 | |
| Operating free-air temperature, $T_A$ | 54 Family | -55 | | 125 | -55 | | 125 | -55 | | 125 | -55 | | 125 | -55 | | 125 | °C |
| | 74 Family | 0 | | 70 | 0 | | 70 | 0 | | 70 | 0 | | 70 | 0 | | 70 | |

## electrical characteristics over recommended operating free-air temperature range (unless otherwise noted)

| PARAMETER | | TEST FIGURE | TEST CONDITIONS[†] | | SERIES 54 / SERIES 74 '02, '25, '27 | | | SERIES 54L / SERIES 74L 'L02 | | | SERIES 54LS / SERIES 74LS 'LS02 'LS27 | | | SERIES 54S / SERIES 74S 'S02, 'S260 | | | UNIT |
|---|---|---|---|---|---|---|---|---|---|---|---|---|---|---|---|---|---|
| | | | | | MIN | TYP[‡] | MAX | MIN | TYP[‡] | MAX | MIN | TYP[‡] | MAX | MIN | TYP[‡] | MAX | |
| $V_{IH}$ High-level input voltage | | 1, 2 | | | 2 | | | 2 | | | 2 | | | 2 | | | V |
| $V_{IL}$ Low-level input voltage | | 1, 2 | | 54 Family | | | 0.8 | | | 0.7 | | | 0.7 | | | 0.8 | V |
| | | | | 74 Family | | | 0.8 | | | 0.7 | | | 0.8 | | | 0.8 | |
| $V_{IK}$ Input clamp voltage | | 3 | $V_{CC}$ = MIN, $I_I$ = § | | | | -1.5 | | | | | | -1.5 | | | -1.2 | V |
| $V_{OH}$ High-level output voltage | | 1 | $V_{CC}$ = MIN, $V_{IL}$ = $V_{IL}$ max, $I_{OH}$ = MAX | 54 Family | 2.4 | 3.4 | | 2.4 | 3.3 | | 2.5 | 3.4 | | 2.5 | 3.4 | | V |
| | | | | 74 Family | 2.4 | 3.4 | | 2.4 | 3.2 | | 2.7 | 3.4 | | 2.7 | 3.4 | | |
| $V_{OL}$ Low-level output voltage | | 2 | $V_{CC}$ = MIN, $V_{IH}$ = 2 V, $I_{OL}$ = MAX | 54 Family | | 0.2 | 0.4 | | 0.15 | 0.3 | | 0.25 | 0.4 | | | 0.5 | V |
| | | | | 74 Family | | 0.2 | 0.4 | | 0.2 | 0.4 | | 0.35 | 0.5 | | | 0.5 | |
| | | | $I_{OL}$ = 4 mA | Series 74LS | | | | | | | | 0.25 | 0.4 | | | | |
| $I_I$ Input current at maximum input voltage | | 4 | $V_{CC}$ = MAX | $V_I$ = 5.5 V | | | 1 | | | 0.1 | | | 0.1 | | | 1 | mA |
| | | | | $V_I$ = 7 V | | | | | | | | | | | | | |
| $I_{IH}$ High-level input current | Data inputs Strobe of '25 | 4 | $V_{CC}$ = MAX | $V_{IH}$ = 2.4 V | | | 40 | | | 10 | | | 20 | | | 50 | µA |
| | All inputs | | | $V_{IH}$ = 2.7 V | | | 160 | | | | | | | | | | |
| $I_{IL}$ Low-level input current | Data inputs Strobe of '25 | 5 | $V_{CC}$ = MAX | $V_{IL}$ = 0.3 V | | | -1.6 | | | -0.18 | | | -0.4 | | | -2 | mA |
| | All inputs | | | $V_{IL}$ = 0.4 V | | | -6.4 | | | | | | | | | | |
| | | | | $V_{IL}$ = 0.5 V | | | | | | | | | | | | | |
| $I_{OS}$ Short-circuit output current[♦] | | 6 | $V_{CC}$ = MAX | 54 Family | -20 | | -55 | -3 | | -15 | -20 | | -100 | -40 | | -100 | mA |
| | | | | 74 Family | -18 | | -55 | -3 | | -15 | -20 | | -100 | -40 | | -100 | |
| $I_{CC}$ Supply current | | 7 | $V_{CC}$ = MAX | | | | | See table on next page | | | | | | | | | mA |

† For conditions shown as MIN or MAX, use the appropriate value specified under recommended operating conditions.
‡ All typical values are at $V_{CC}$ = 5 V, $T_A$ = 25°C.
§ $I_I$ = -12 mA for SN54'/SN74' and -18 mA for SN54LS'/SN74LS' and SN54S'/SN74S'.
♦ Not more than one output should be shorted at a time, and for SN54LS'/SN74LS' and SN54S'/SN74S', duration of output short-circuit should not exceed one second.

## recommended operating conditions

| PARAMETER | | SERIES 54 / SERIES 74 '00, '04, '10, '20, '30 | | | SERIES 54H / SERIES 74H 'H00, 'H04, 'H10, 'H20, 'H30 | | | SERIES 54L / SERIES 74L 'L00, 'L04, 'L10, 'L20, 'L30 | | | SERIES 54LS / SERIES 74LS 'LS00, 'LS04, 'LS10, 'LS20, 'LS30 | | | SERIES 54S / SERIES 74S 'S00, 'S04, 'S10, 'S20, 'S30, 'S133 | | | UNIT |
|---|---|---|---|---|---|---|---|---|---|---|---|---|---|---|---|---|---|
| | | MIN | NOM | MAX | MIN | NOM | MAX | MIN | NOM | MAX | MIN | NOM | MAX | MIN | NOM | MAX | |
| Supply voltage, $V_{CC}$ | 54 Family | 4.5 | 5 | 5.5 | 4.5 | 5 | 5.5 | 4.5 | 5 | 5.5 | 4.5 | 5 | 5.5 | 4.5 | 5 | 5.5 | V |
| | 74 Family | 4.75 | 5 | 5.25 | 4.75 | 5 | 5.25 | 4.75 | 5 | 5.25 | 4.75 | 5 | 5.25 | 4.75 | 5 | 5.25 | |
| High-level output current, $I_{OH}$ | 54 Family | | | −400 | | | −500 | | | −100 | | | −400 | | | −1000 | µA |
| | 74 Family | | | −400 | | | −500 | | | −200 | | | −400 | | | −1000 | |
| Low-level output current, $I_{OL}$ | 54 Family | | | 16 | | | 20 | | | 2 | | | 4 | | | 20 | mA |
| | 74 Family | | | 16 | | | 20 | | | 3.6 | | | 8 | | | 20 | |
| Operating free-air temperature, $T_A$ | 54 Family | −55 | | 125 | −55 | | 125 | −55 | | 125 | −55 | | 125 | −55 | | 125 | °C |
| | 74 Family | 0 | | 70 | 0 | | 70 | 0 | | 70 | 0 | | 70 | 0 | | 70 | |

## electrical characteristics over recommended operating free-air temperature range (unless otherwise noted)

| PARAMETER | TEST FIGURE | TEST CONDITIONS† | SERIES 54 / SERIES 74 '00, '04, '10, '20, '30 | | | SERIES 54H / SERIES 74H 'H00, 'H04, 'H10, 'H20, 'H30 | | | SERIES 54L / SERIES 74L 'L00, 'L04, 'L10, 'L20, 'L30 | | | SERIES 54LS / SERIES 74LS 'LS00, 'LS04, 'LS10, 'LS20, 'LS30 | | | SERIES 54S / SERIES 74S 'S00, 'S04, 'S10, 'S20, 'S30, 'S133 | | | UNIT |
|---|---|---|---|---|---|---|---|---|---|---|---|---|---|---|---|---|---|---|
| | | | MIN | TYP‡ | MAX | MIN | TYP‡ | MAX | MIN | TYP‡ | MAX | MIN | TYP‡ | MAX | MIN | TYP‡ | MAX | |
| $V_{IH}$ High-level input voltage | 1, 2 | | 2 | | | 2 | | | 2 | | | 2 | | | 2 | | | V |
| $V_{IL}$ Low-level input voltage | 1, 2 | 54 Family | | | 0.8 | | | 0.8 | | | 0.7 | | | 0.7 | | | 0.8 | V |
| | | 74 Family | | | 0.8 | | | 0.8 | | | 0.7 | | | 0.8 | | | 0.8 | |
| $V_{IK}$ Input clamp voltage | 3 | $V_{CC}$ = MIN, $I_I$ = § | | | −1.5 | | | −1.5 | | | | | | −1.5 | | | −1.2 | V |
| $V_{OH}$ High-level output voltage | 1 | $V_{CC}$ = MIN, $V_{IL}$ = $V_{IL}$ max, $I_{OH}$ = MAX | 2.4 | 3.4 | | 2.4 | 3.5 | | 2.4 | 3.3 | | 2.5 | 3.4 | | 2.5 | 3.4 | | V |
| | | | 2.4 | 3.4 | | 2.4 | 3.5 | | 2.4 | 3.2 | | 2.7 | 3.4 | | 2.7 | 3.4 | | |
| $V_{OL}$ Low-level output voltage | 2 | $V_{CC}$ = MIN, $V_{IH}$ = 2 V, $I_{OL}$ = MAX | | 0.2 | 0.4 | | 0.2 | 0.4 | | 0.15 | 0.3 | | 0.25 | 0.4 | | | 0.5 | V |
| | | | | 0.2 | 0.4 | | 0.2 | 0.4 | | 0.2 | 0.4 | | 0.25 | 0.5 | | | 0.5 | |
| | | $I_{OL}$ = 4 mA Series 74LS | | | | | | | | | | | | 0.4 | | | | |
| $I_I$ Input current at maximum input voltage | 4 | $V_{CC}$ = MAX, $V_I$ = 5.5 V / $V_I$ = 7 V | | | 1 | | | 1 | | | 0.1 | | | 0.1 | | | 1 | mA |
| $I_{IH}$ High-level input current | 4 | $V_{CC}$ = MAX, $V_{IH}$ = 2.4 V / 2.7 V | | | 40 | | | 50 | | | 10 | | | 20 | | | 50 | µA |
| $I_{IL}$ Low-level input current | 5 | $V_{CC}$ = MAX, $V_{IL}$ = 0.4 V / 0.3 V / 0.5 V | | | −1.6 | | | −2 | | | −0.18 | | | −0.4 | | | −2 | mA |
| $I_{OS}$ Short-circuit output current◆ | 6 | $V_{CC}$ = MAX | −20 | | −55 | −40 | | −100 | −3 | | −15 | −20 | | −100 | −40 | | −100 | mA |
| | | | −18 | | −55 | −40 | | −100 | −3 | | −15 | −20 | | −100 | −40 | | −100 | |
| $I_{CC}$ Supply current | 7 | $V_{CC}$ = MAX | See table on next page | | | | | | | | | | | | | | | mA |

† For conditions shown as MIN or MAX, use the appropriate value specified under recommended operating conditions.
‡ All typical values are at $V_{CC}$ = 5 V, $T_A$ = 25°C.
§ $I_I$ = −12 mA for SN54'/SN74', −8 mA for SN54LS'/SN74LS', and −18 mA for SN54H'/SN74H', and for SN54H'/SN74H', SN54LS'/SN74LS', and SN54S'/SN74S'.
◆ Not more than one output should be shorted at a time, and for SN54H'/SN74H', SN54LS'/SN74LS', and SN54S'/SN74S', duration of short-circuit should not exceed 1 second.

# GLOSSARY

**accumulator**   register that stores data for use by the CPU

**address**   location in memory of a computer

**alphanumeric display**   LED display that can show both numbers and letters

**American Standard Code for Information Interchange (ASCII)**   a popular alphanumeric code for transmitting letters, numbers, symbols, and keyboard functions

**analog circuits**   circuits that vary continuously over a range from high to low rather than having two set values

**AND**   logic gate that requires highs at all inputs to produce a high output

**arithmetic logic unit (ALU)**   part of the CPU that does calculations

**assembly language**   a method of giving instructions to a computer using two- to four-letter abbreviated words that are called mnemonics

**binary**   two-digit number system

**binary coded decimal**   number system using binary numbers from 0 to 9 in each column

**binary ripple counter**   binary counter in which one flip-flop provides the clock pulse for the next

**bit**   smallest unit of memory (either A1 or 0)

**Boolean algebra**   branch of mathematics invented by George Boole

**bus**   connection used to carry data between points in a computer

**byte**   eight successive bits

**capacitor**   a device that stores electric charge

**capillary action**   air pressure on the surface of a liquid forces the liquid up into a small tube

**cascading**   connecting one IC so that it controls the next one

**central processing unit (CPU)**   section of a computer that receives data, manipulates it, and sends it to the output

**clock input**   pulse that controls when the inputs change the output

**CMOS**   complementary metal oxide semiconductors

**coating**   chemical used to sensitize PC boards

**cold solder joint**   soldered area that does not make a good connection because the solder does not adhere to the desired surfaces

**D flip-flop**   type of flip-flop that has only one input

**decade counter**   counter that counts ten numbers, then recycles

**decoding**   the process of selecting a particular binary number from a series of binary numbers

**decoding counter**   digital logic counter that can select one number from a group of numbers

**demultiplexer**   a device that separates data obtained from a few lines and distributes it correctly to several lines

**diode**   device that allows electrons to flow in only one direction

**dot-matrix display**   display of thirty-five or more LEDs to show numbers or letters

**down counter**   counter that counts backward

**DTL**   diode transistor logic

**electrical shock**   reaction of nerves and muscles to current passing through the body

**electricity**   movement of electrons through a conductor

**electron**   smallest unit of an atom; it orbits around the nucleus

**encoding**   process of electronically converting from one code to another

**EPROM (eraseable programmable read only memory)**   memory that can be changed by using ultraviolet light

**etch-resist transfers**   rub-on patterns to use in making printed circuit board patterns

**Exclusive NOR (XNOR)**   logic gate that produces a high output when both inputs are high

**Exclusive OR (XOR)**   logic gate that produces a low output when both inputs are high

**FET**   field effect transistors

**fetch**   one of the first instructions to a computer (used to get data or instructions out of memory)

**fibrillation**   irregular heartbeat

**filament**   element that gives off heat when electricity flows through it

**floating high**   condition of an input when no connection is made

**flux**   chemical used in soldering to clean metal

**frequency dividers**   digital logic circuit used to change the frequency to a lower level

**full adder**   logic circuit capable of adding three inputs together

**germanium**   grayish white brittle element used in ICs

**gray code**   special binary code

**half adder**   adder capable of adding two bits

**heat sink**   alligator clips or other metal surface used to carry away excess heat during soldering

**hertz**   cycle per second

**hexadecimal**   sixteen-digit number system

**high**   positive 5 volts; equal to 1 in digital logic

**initialization**   first steps a computer takes before processing data

**integrated circuit**   circuit containing one or several components and built into a small chip

**inverter**   logic gate that produces an output opposite the input

**involatile**   keeps data when the power is shut off

**JK flip-flop**   see master-slave flip-flop

**leading edge**   the start of a clock pulse as it goes from low to high

**light-emitting diode (LED)**   a semiconductor that allows electricity to flow in one direction only thus giving off energy as light

**line voltage**   117 volts

**liquid crystal display (LCD)**   a display showing the output used in watches, etc.

**logic gates**   electrical device with one or more inputs and one output

**low**   zero voltage; a 0 in a logic circuit

**LSB**   least significant bit

**LSI**   large scale integration of components in a microchip

**machine language**   instructions given to a computer in 1s or 0s

**master-slave**   flip-flop circuit (JK circuit) in which the slave acts in response to the action of the master

**microchip**   another name for an IC

**microcomputer**   computer that uses a microprocessor

**microprocessor**   one or more chips that can handle manipulations of data, etc.

**mini floppy disc**   5¼-inch, disc-shaped magnetic storage device

**mnemonics**   three- to five-letter words used as instructions to the computer

**modulo counter**   circuit designed to count to a certain number and recycle

**MOS**   metal oxide semiconductors

**MSB**   most significant bit

**MSI**   medium scale integration in an IC

**multiplexers**   group of logic gates that takes several inputs and output them one at a time through one output line

**NAND**   logic gate that produces a low output when all inputs are high

**NOR**   logic gate that produces a high output when all inputs are low

**N-type**   negative material used in making a transistor

**octal**   base-8 number system

**optical character recognition (OCR)**   process used to read and interpret pages of text

**OR**   logic gate producing a high output when one or more of the inputs is high

**parallel-load shift registers**   shift register in which all of the data can be entered simultaneously

**passive integrated transponder**   silicon chip preprogrammed with a code used for fast identification

**pin-out**   diagram showing interconnections of circuitry

**pixels**   dots on a video screen

**printed circuit board (PCB)** fiberglass or phenolic board with a layer of copper that can be etched

**program** set of instructions to a computer

**program counter** counter that keeps steps in order

**PROM (programmable read only memory)** can be programmed by user but cannot be changed

**P-type material** positive material used in making transistors

**quad** four

**RAM** random access memory

**read** to retrieve data from memory

**resistor-ladder network** resistor circuitry used to convert from a digital circuit to an analog circuit

**resistor** electrical device that opposes the flow of electrons

**ROM (read only memory)** once programmed into the memory, data can be retrieved but not changed

**RS flip-flop** logic circuit used for memory that has set and reset inputs

**R 2R ladder** a circuit to convert digital to analog

**schematic diagram** diagram showing symbols and connections

**scratch** built entirely by builder, including etching of PC board and assembling of individual parts

**semiconductor** material that is neither a good conductor nor a good insulator

**serial-load shift registers** data must be shifted one bit at a time

**seven-segment display** device made up of seven LEDs used to show the numbers 0 through 9

**shift registers** series of flip-flops used for temporary data storage in which data can be moved (shifted) to the right or left

**silicon** element used in ICs

**SSI** small scale integration of ICs

**summing amplifier** a circuit that converts a small current flow to an amplified voltage

**synchronous counter** binary counter in which flip-flops receive the clock pulse simultaneously

**thermionic emission** discharge from a material when it is heated

**traces** copper connections between components on a PCB

**trailing edge** last part of the clock pulse as it goes from high to low

**transistor** component made of semiconductors and used for amplifying or switching

**triode** three-element vacuum tube

**truth table** listing of all possible inputs and their corresponding outputs

**TTL**   transistor-transistor logic

**video monitor**   screen that displays the output of a computer (much
     like a television set)

**VLSI**   very large scale integration of an IC

**volatile**   loses data when the power is turned off

**voltage**   electrical pressure

**word**   group of bits

**write**   to enter data into memory

# INDEX